Hampshire the New Forest Stories of the Supernatural

Sonia Smith

COUNTRYSIDE BOOKS
NEWBURY, BERKSHIRE

COUNTRYSIDE BOOKS
3 Catherine Road
Newbury, Berkshire

To view our complete range of books,
please visit us at
www.countrysidebooks.co.uk

ISBN 978 1 84674 164 7

Designed by Peter Davies, Nautilus Design

Produced through MRM Associates Ltd., Reading
Typeset by Mac Style, Beverley, E. Yorkshire
Printed by Information Press

Contents

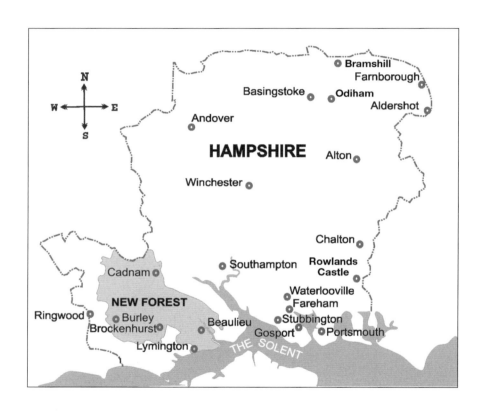

Introduction

After I had finished writing *Wiltshire Stories of the Supernatural*, I began to look at my stored research notes, letters and emails from interested people in other parts of the country. It soon became apparent to me that I had many stories from my contacts in the New Forest and Hampshire areas – and I also have relatives and friends who live there.

Hampshire and the New Forest area, which incidentally is one of my favourite places, is as steeped in tales of the supernatural as I had found Wiltshire to be. All of the stories in this book are authentic and many have been told to me verbally by the people involved. I have used artistic licence in the writing of them, to make them more readable, but all of the basic facts of the strange happenings are true. Fact, in these cases, is indeed stranger than fiction. Incredible as it may seem, these things really happened.

I have occasionally changed the names of the actual people concerned in the tales, at their request. It seems that, even today, there can still be a stigma attached to individuals who have had a supernatural experience. Many are afraid that they will be classed as 'barmy' by those around them if they own up to such things. This really is a pity, as it does stop some amazing accounts of true experiences coming to light.

Sometimes there are financial or business reasons for not wishing to divulge actual names or places, as in the case of 'The Ghostly Pianist'. The visiting ladies had the distinct impression that the owners of the hotel they stayed in felt that a ghostly pianist might not be good for trade! Of course, today it might have been used quite in the opposite way, as haunted pubs and hotels frequently attract paranormal investigators and curious tourists!

In the case of 'The Haunted Cottage', it was felt by the family concerned that the actual geographical position of the cottage ought to be kept secret. After all, the farmer would have needed another tenant/farm worker to live there after they had fled; and still would today. They told me that they sincerely hoped that the place would have been exorcised, for everyone's sake.

Some of the other stories retain the actual names of the participants and places concerned. I always feel so honoured that people open up to me and tell these amazing tales for me to record, that others might share them. Often this brings in more letters and emails from people who say that they have had similar experiences in the same places. It is astonishing to find, when doing research on these matters, that some of the supernatural encounters have been experienced, much in the same way, at another date and by different people who do not know one another.

I finish this introduction by saying a thank you to all those people who have related these tales to me and made this book possible. I hope this collection of experiences goes some way to demonstrating that the supernatural is very much here amongst us. Perhaps, one day, science will catch up and give us an answer as to why such things occur. But until then, I think we can safely say that these unexplained happenings will remain a delicious mystery that sends a shiver down our spine when we read about them.

Sonia Smith

1

The Werewolf of Southampton

In 1971 Priscilla Morgan was working as a cleaner at Southampton University, which was near her home. A very efficient and scrupulous lady, she was usually responsible for, amongst other things, the archaeological department, as she worked with great care and could be trusted amongst the valuable items that resided there.

The events of this story resulted from the arrival in the department of some strange – and what some members of staff described as evil looking – artefacts, two stone heads. They had been sent to be examined by one of the university's experts, who specialised in paganism. The heads were both only a little larger than tennis balls and had been found by some children who had been digging in the garden of a council house in Hexham, Northumberland.

No one liked the look of these heads, which had, strangely enough, arrived in a little coffin-shaped box. It was even whispered by some of the staff that the prominent lady archaeologist who was to examine them had taken a severe dislike to them herself, despite her natural interest.

Priscilla, a very down-to-earth type of woman, laughed when she heard of this fuss. She had seen many strange items in the department over the years when doing her cleaning work, some of which had certainly given her what she called the 'heebie jeebies'. But, as she always confirmed to her husband Jack, she was not superstitious in any way. Ghosts, bogies, curses, and other such nonsense that she had heard spoken of by some of the other staff held no sway over her.

In fact, quite the opposite. Jack and she would have a good laugh together over a beer at the local pub about some of the tales that the other members of staff had told her of supernatural things, connected to some of the objects that arrived at the university. She thought these people had far too vivid an imagination, and she believed that they just liked a story; and firmly told them so.

It was without trepidation therefore that Priscilla set off to do her evening cleaning duties at the university as usual, one rather rainy evening, soon after the heads had arrived there. She entered the archaeological department and went to the cupboard to get out her cleaning tools, ready for work. Tonight she was going to polish all the glass display cases. This was one of her favourite jobs. She took immense pride in the fact that she could clean the glass to a sparkle, without leaving behind even one little smear.

She hummed to herself as she worked, thinking of the weekend to come. It was her daughter's engagement party, and Priscilla was in charge of getting the food sorted. She was just deciding on whether to get mini pork pies or do vol-au-vents, when she suddenly realised that, despite the warm room, she had goose pimples. She gave an involuntary little shudder, frowned, shrugged her shoulders, and carried on polishing.

Then she got the feeling that there was someone in the room watching her. She shrugged this off too. How ridiculous she was being! No one else was, or could be, in the room. She was perfectly alone. It was then that she turned to see the much discussed primitive-looking stone heads, sitting inconspicuously together, next to their little coffin-shaped box, on one of the desk tops. Priscilla had to admit, in spite of herself, that there was something quite malevolent about them. She shuddered again. Why was she feeling cold? She shook herself. She must break the spell.

'You look like two horrible little buggers!' she said aloud, with as much humour as she could muster. But, as the two evil-looking heads stared back at her, her voice trailed off, despite her conviction. She had to admit that she did not feel very comfortable around them.

She finished her work much quicker than usual that night. She really just wanted to go home. Unusual for her, as she generally liked to sit down after she had finished and have a coffee from the machine and a cigarette. She hurried through her chores, and felt really thankful that she was soon packing up her cleaning materials in readiness to leave. She rubbed her arms with her hands before she opened the exit door from the archaeology department. Then suddenly she smiled to herself and said, 'It's all them stories. That's all it is. Them daft sods wi' their stories! Priscilla Morgan, buck up girl!' She felt reassured by her own words. The creeping fear had started to subside.

It was only when she actually went through the door that she had a feeling that something had passed her. It was the same feeling that you get when a dog slips by in front of you as you open the door to go out. Only a strange sensation came with it – a dark suspicion that she could not describe. And she definitely felt cold again. And, out of the periphery of her vision, she thought that she had seen a large black shape speedily disappearing down an adjoining corridor.

Priscilla was glad to get back home that night. The house was empty as Jack was at their local, playing darts, and Vivianne, their daughter, was out with her fiancé. Priscilla, still feeling uneasy, put on all the lights in the house even though it was not yet quite dark, and then brewed a large pot of tea. She stoked up the Rayburn and sat right next to it. She was beginning to feel a little more normal now. All the way home she had somehow had the feeling that there was something with her. Not exactly following her, but there at her side one moment, the next bounding ahead, or coming along behind her, the way a pet dog might do. But this thing was not like a pet dog. No, this thing had a very sinister feel to it. She had actually seen nothing at all. No, it was all feeling. She had felt its presence, not seen it. And its presence had not been pleasant.

She had been so pleased to shut the front door on the night. She felt a lot better now, as she sipped her hot tea, and she gave herself a talking to. It was just those stories from the rest of them. That was all. She must stop thinking like this. It was daft, that's what it was. Daft.

Soon Vivianne was back. She breezed in, kissing her mother's cheek, poured herself a cup of tea and went up to her room to ponder over her party list. She shouted down to ask her mother if she had booked the back room of the pub in readiness. Her mother affirmed – for the umpteenth time – that she had. Priscilla felt warm again; normality had returned.

Not long after, Jack came home too, rosy of face, and his voice a little louder than usual. Priscilla asked her husband if the beer had been good that night. Jack retorted that it certainly had. They had opened a new cask of fine strong ale, and the locals all got a pint for free to celebrate the coming engagement! They both laughed and Priscilla complained about not being there to join in, but with good humour.

Jack noticed that his wife was a little more reserved than usual and asked if she was all right. Priscilla said that she was, but that she was feeling a little chilled. Jack saw that the Rayburn had been well stoked and wondered if his wife might be going down with a cold.

Vivianne came in, declaring that she had left her muddied boots outside the front door and had better retrieve them in case there was more rain or the morning dew soaked them.

What happened next froze Priscilla to her chair and sent Jack bolting through the front door as if the Devil was after him. Vivianne was screaming, and then she ran back into the kitchen pale and shaken, her boots dangling from one hand. 'There's some sort of big animal out there!' she cried, eyes wide, her breathing accelerated.

Priscilla swallowed hard, thinking of the evening's events. Jack came back in looking puzzled, and not a little afraid. 'I thought I saw something racing down the road. It moved like an animal … but it looked a bit like a man.'

The three of them were silent then. They just stood looking at each other with questioning glances. Priscilla's mind whirred. Suddenly Vivianne dropped her boots and said, 'Perhaps an animal has escaped from somewhere, a circus or something maybe. Should we call the police? Won't they get some wildlife experts in or something?' Jack sat down suddenly with relief. 'That'll be about it,' he said, 'our Viv is right.' Priscilla still said nothing.

Jack called the police station. The duty sergeant thanked him for his call, but said that there had been no reports of any escaped animal and there were no other sightings to date. Jack remained insistent and the sergeant promised to send someone round the next day to investigate.

He recommended, meanwhile, that Jack and his family should stay indoors in case there was any danger from a wild beast.

Still Priscilla said nothing. She didn't know how to broach the subject. And anyway, how could two stone heads in the archaeology department at the university have anything to do with some strange animal outside? She knew inside that somehow these things were connected. But she didn't know how, and she certainly did not know how to start to tell the rest of her family.

'Anyway,' said Jack, locking both the front door and the back. 'Time for bed, I reckon. That's enough excitement for tonight. Perhaps the wildlife people will come out and catch that poor ol' animal tomorrow.'

Vivianne went and kissed first her father's cheek, and then her mother's. She said goodnight to them both and went up to bed. Jack looked across at his wife and wondered if a nightcap might be in order. He went and poured himself a whisky but Priscilla refused. So he drank his down and said, 'Oh well, up the old wooden hill for me.'

Priscilla assured him that she would join him very soon. So he left her there, sitting by the Rayburn. Seeing that she looked tense and a little shocked, he thought she might need time to settle before going to bed. 'Don't be too long up, love,' he said with concern before leaving the room.

Priscilla did not know how long she slept there in the chair, but the Rayburn had not been shut down for the night, so had burnt low. Something woke her but she was very unsure as to what. Her heart was pounding and she thought that she had heard Vivianne's voice calling to her. She ran into the hallway to see her daughter at the top of the stairs, her face pale, and with a horrified expression. But it was what was at the bottom of the stairs that made her mouth go dry with fear.

A huge man, or was it an animal, stood there. It was over six feet in height and seemed to have the top half of a wolf and the bottom half of a man. It was covered with what looked like thick black fur. It glared at her for a minute with yellow-green eyes that showed no particular emotion. It then turned tail and bounded back up the stairs towards Vivianne.

Priscilla's mouth had now become so dry that she could make no sound, although she badly wanted to scream. Not so Vivianne, who let out a fearful sound as the thing ran past her and into her bedroom. She turned to see it jump right out of her open window and bound off at speed into the darkness.

The next day a police officer came to speak to the shocked family. The garden was checked but despite the recent rain there were no footprints. Jack was beside himself and was very annoyed when the policeman asked if Mrs Morgan and Miss Morgan had ever suffered from any form of hysteria. He told the officer that he could not think of a woman less likely to suffer from hysterics than his wife. The police officer gently said that the two ladies' statements had been rather bizarre when it came to describing the animal they had seen. Jack was still insistent that something ought to be done. The policeman shrugged his shoulders and said that he had no evidence of any animal tracks, or human for that matter, except of course their own. And there had been no other reports in their area of any similar incidents.

Nothing was the same again after this for the Morgan family. They found themselves jittery in their own home at night. Priscilla gave up her cleaning job at the university and went and worked in a local shop instead. Eventually they decided to move. The house could never feel the same to them again.

It was some years later that Priscilla read an interesting article about a prominent archaeologist and expert on paganism whom she knew had worked at Southampton University. It was said that the archaeologist had taken what were termed the two Hexham Heads from the university to her own home to do some work examining them. Some very strange events happened whilst they were under her roof, including a sighting of a terrifying creature – seen not only by the archaeologist herself, but also by some other members of her family. This creature was described as being half man, half wolf … in other words, a werewolf.

2

The Mirror

In the autumn of 1991, Stella Thornton was married to Tom Barron. They were making their home in London and Stella had declared that she wished to spend their two week honeymoon travelling around the New Forest, an area she had often visited with her parents as a child. It was full of happy memories: gorse and moor; forest and stream; ponies, donkeys, and huge pigs turned loose to feed on the acorns at the end of summer. Stella said that this was the place of her heart, her spiritual home.

It seemed the most natural thing in the world to return there and share the forest's beauty and magic with someone who was so very special to her – Tom, her new husband. So off they had set after their wedding celebrations, in their little MG sports car, which was still full of handfuls of pink confetti that Stella had refused to let Tom vacuum out.

Stella's heart lifted when they reached the New Forest. She felt like a young girl again. The awesome oaks and the stately beeches were already changing their green mantles for ones of red and gold. The foals were already leggy and tall, and had filled out on the rich milk of the mares. There was a heady sweet richness on the air as if autumn came with a golden breath.

Stella and Tom went here, there and everywhere, Stella squealing and begging to stop at remembered places. They walked in the muted autumn sunshine, hand in hand. Stella would reach down and stroke the great male ferns and marvel at their delicacy, yet how strong they were too. Tom, pointing and holding his breath as they saw a stag and two hinds come out into the forest clearing in front of them – noses quivering, dainty forefoot lifted, listening, before gracefully leaping away.

Tom was glad now that he had not gone on trying to persuade Stella to honeymoon abroad. He had never been to the New Forest, and thought it as truly stunning as his new wife had said that it was. He was happy and relaxed, leaving behind for a while his stressful and high-powered job.

He looked at Stella as they walked. He had never seen her so radiant; no, not even on their wedding day. Her lovely, long auburn hair the colour that the leaves on the trees had become. She was tall and slender as a willow branch, her amber eyes bright as a robin's. He had not seen it before but, coming here, she looked like a child of the forest – an elf girl!

Glancing up, Stella saw Tom's eyes on her. And suddenly, when she looked back at him, there was a pang in her heart that she couldn't understand. He stood there amongst the trees – tall and very dark, English, with the air of an Italian. He was as elegant in his old tee shirt and jeans as he was in his well-cut office suits. Tom could look good in anything. His dark eyes were full of tenderness as he gazed at her.

Suddenly Stella found that there were tears in her eyes and began to wonder what in the world she would ever do without him. Then she blinked back the tears and chastised herself for having such morbid thoughts at such a happy time. She was a silly goose, that is what she was. She raced over to him, flinging her arms about him; and they embraced for what seemed like an aeon, as only lovers can. And the world stood still and nothing else really mattered.

The weather held out that September to give Stella and Tom two glorious weeks. They had gone pony trekking. Tom had fallen off; he had never been on a horse before in his life. Stella, a good horsewoman, had laughed and told him that you must fall off seven, and get on eight, times before you could say you were on your way to being a good rider. Tom had done some fishing. And Stella, a talented artist, had sat on the riverbank painting the scene in pale watercolours, everything merging together on the paper; no difference between water and sky; Tom's back a part of the rich autumnal land.

On the last day of the holiday, Stella begged to go and have lunch in the Red Lion pub at Chalton on their way back. As a child she had always stopped there with her parents and her sister Maeve, before their journey home. Tom was dubious. He longed for a London restaurant where the food and wine would be to his taste. He wanted to end the honeymoon with a really fabulous meal. He was ready now to return to their new home, and he knew of a place to eat not so far from where they lived. But Stella had looked so crestfallen at his suggestion that Tom immediately gave in, if only because a face as beautiful as Stella's should always be smiling.

So they went to the Red Lion just as Stella had wanted. It was a beautiful old thatched inn with an original fireplace that was quite spectacular. Tom could see that Stella was very happy. She looked delicious in an apple green, full-skirted silk dress and her city heels. After a drink, he began to be pleased that they had come – the old pub had an atmosphere all of its own.

Stella ordered a pudding, much to Tom's surprise, as she was not known for her sweet tooth. Then she said she had to go and powder her nose. Stella went into the ladies and used the toilet. She came out of the cubicle, washed her hands, opened her dainty green patent leather handbag and searched for a lipstick. She looked into the old, and rather strange, mirror that hung on the wall. It was spotted with time, and mercury-backed. It shone as only real mercury-backed mirrors can; but this one had an almost uncanny shine. She applied her lipstick. She ruffled her hair with her hands. She could see her own reflection looking quizzically back.

Stella stood there just staring into the mirror. Then, although she knew that there was no other person in the room with her, she saw the reflection of a woman who appeared to be standing directly behind her. Stella, feeling rather afraid, slowly turned to make sure there was really no one behind her. No. There was no one in the room with her. But when she turned back to the mirror the reflection of the woman was still there.

The face stared back at her, unmoving. The woman was dressed all in black, in what looked like Victorian-style clothes. Her hair was auburn, like Stella's own hair. But it was pulled back from her face and pinned, with a frame of curls left around her cheeks. Her eyes were large, luminous, and sad. Her complexion was pale and, again, similar to Stella, in the fact that she had a sprinkle of faint freckles across the top of her cheeks and the bridge of her nose.

Stella stood mesmerised. She could feel the hairs rising on the back of her neck. The temperature in the room had dropped. It felt like a December day. The woman in the mirror continued to stare steadily back at Stella in a most unnerving way. Stella wanted to run out of the room, but it was as if she were frozen to the spot. So she just stood there, staring into the mirror. Staring at a ghost.

Then, as she watched, the woman raised a pale white hand, displaying a black-edged card. Words were on it in black ink. Stella strained her eyes to read the words. Eventually she saw

NOVEMBER 8th

The woman's image then disappeared from the mirror and Stella felt the room regain its warmth. She was suddenly overcome by a sensation of supreme dread, and felt sick and quite faint. She took out a pen and a scrap of paper from her bag and wrote the words as she had seen them. She held them to the mirror. 'NOVEMBER 8th'.

The door opened and a young woman entered. 'Are you ok? Your husband asked me to come in and see if you were all right as you have been in here some time.'

Stella quickly hid the pen and paper in her bag. 'Yes. I … I came over a little faint. I think I am all right now, thanks.'

'You are on your honeymoon, aren't you? Your husband said. Been overdoing it?' She gave a knowing glance.

'Maybe.' Stella tried to smile.

Stella went straight over to Tom and asked to leave. Tom was very surprised at this, as the Red Lion stop had all been Stella's idea. But he could see that she looked unwell, so he did not remonstrate, but asked for the bill and they left.

On the way home Tom asked if Stella was feeling all right. Stella told him what had happened, suddenly relieved at being able to talk about it. Tom looked very concerned for a few moments. Then he burst out laughing. 'Artists, my darling, are renowned for their over-active imagination,' he said, without unkindness.

Stella did not speak of the incident again. But the feeling of dread she had experienced would not leave her. It seemed to build. As the weeks went by, she felt it like a heavy stone sitting on her solar plexus. The happiness of the honeymoon had been blighted by some darkness that she could not explain. She had become anxious and could not concentrate on her work.

Then, Tom came home one night exhilarated. He was to go to see an important business client down in Exeter. He would be away from home for only a couple of nights. If the deal went right, it could make them quite rich. Stella proclaimed that they were quite well off enough, did he have to go? Tom could not believe she was saying this to him. He was an ambitious man. Did she ever want to start a family or not? They would need money if she did.

Stella had to give in. She could see that Tom would not move on this. How could she tell him how anxious she felt when she really did not know why she felt that way? Stella asked when it was he was to travel to Exeter.

'The 8th of November,' said Tom.

Stella blanched at this. She flung her arms around her husband, clinging tight, crying, begging him not to go. Tom, for once, was furious with her. He loved Stella dearly, but this was too much. Some silly imagined happening in a Hampshire pub could not stand in the way of something so important as this. Couldn't she see that? Their future was at stake. He might never get another chance as good as this. He was a little gentler after the first initial anger; explaining that she was an artist after all. It was her over-vivid imagination, that was all.

Stella still continued to beg her husband not to go, right up to the day of his leaving. He found this hard to contend with. But felt that she must not win on this. It was too important. So, before he drove off to Exeter he came into their bedroom and kissed her, hugging her tight, trying to alleviate her fears. 'I'll call you as soon as I arrive. I promise.' She clung to him like a little child and cried. He had to prize her hands from him.

They were the last words she ever heard from him. A policeman, accompanied by a policewoman, came to their house that evening. They had bad news. Tom had died in a car accident. It was, of course, the 8th of November.

3

The Gypsy Curse

Gypsies have always been very much part of New Forest life, the Ringwood horse sales being one of the main attractions for these people to meet, make merry, and sell some of their sought after true gypsy ponies.

Before the strict regulations of the present day, there would often be large groups of these nomads, who would turn up in their brightly-painted, horse-drawn wagons – the famous gypsy caravans. They would find certain clearings in the forest where they would camp, sometimes for several weeks, or even months. Sometimes there would be groups meeting up from all over the West Country, and perhaps from even further afield.

This story begins when Patricia Mandrell and her husband Derek went camping in the Ringwood area of the New Forest.

It was a rather rainy summer in the early 1960s. Patricia and Derek had managed to save their hard-earned money and purchased a camper van. At the time they lived in Downton so they decided to try out their new acquisition by going for a long weekend in the New Forest, before venturing a greater distance with it.

They took their dog, a brindled whippet by the name of Midge, along with them. All three got rather excited as they set out in their smart new vehicle. It was around six o'clock in the evening by the time they had chosen a spot to park. Derek immediately wanted to take the camping stove out into a nearby clearing to do what he called a 'fabulous fry up'. It had been raining and it was chilly, despite it being late July, so Derek decided that a fire might be in order. Being a very conscientious man, he promptly made a circle of stones to keep the fire completely safe from spreading, although the likelihood of that happening was not very great, it being such a wet summer.

Personally, Patricia wanted to stay inside the camper van but she gave in to Derek's cajoling, but mainly to Midge's, who was giving her the 'sad eyes' treatment, which meant that she wanted to go out and run around, but would not do so without her mistress. Midge just loved to go looking for rabbits.

As Derek got the camping stove going and began to sort through the boxes for bacon, sausages and eggs, Patricia told him that she would take Midge for a run and they would look for some dry sticks for the fire, if they could find any. Midge was dancing around her feet, dying to go zig-zagging through the trees, and run just for the joy of it, as her breed often do.

So Patricia set off amongst the tall, stately trees, their green leaves dripping still from the fine summer rain, the kind of rain that permeates just about everything. She bent to pick up sticks several times along the way, but soon found that she had to discard them again, as they were quite sodden. Midge ran ahead, in and out of the bushes, round and round the trees, crashing through the ferns at high speed, sometimes stopping momentarily, sniffing for her prey.

Then, just as Patricia had paused beneath a beech tree to pick up a drier branch she had found, Midge came running back to her, tail held very tightly to her backside, ears flat to her head. 'Now then Midge,' said Patricia, absently patting her dog, 'how have you scared yourself this time?' Patricia laughed a little; whippets are not renowned for their courage. Midge huddled into the legs of her mistress. She trembled, as whippets will, one front leg lifted, gazing out towards the trees from whence she had come.

'What is it? What is it, you silly old thing?' Patricia asked, feeling a little uneasy. Then, suddenly, she saw a young girl walking amongst the trees. She was about 100 yards away from where Patricia and Midge were standing. She was rather tall and was dressed in a long black skirt, with a bright red woollen shawl about her shoulders. She had dark hair, olive skin and a pretty face, except she seemed quite forlorn and walked with her head bowed, as if in sorrow. She looked about 17 years old.

Patricia began to wonder if she was lost. There was no one else in sight, and she had no dog with her either. Or maybe she was unhappy in some way and needed help? Patricia decided to go over and speak to her, to ask her if she was all right, and walked towards the girl, whistling softly to Midge to follow. But, strangely, Midge would not move. Midge, who always followed her everywhere, would not move. The dog just stood trembling, looking directly at the girl.

Then a weird thing happened. The girl completely disappeared! Patricia ran this way and that, calling out, but she was nowhere to be seen. It would have been impossible not to spot that bright red shawl but there was no sign of anyone. An eerie silence seemed to descend. Patricia suddenly shivered. She had a feeling in the pit of her stomach that she remembered clearly from the past. It was when, as a child, she had seen a strange figure standing on the landing of her parents' house. She had seen a ghost.

Patricia was quite shaken. She ran immediately back to Derek, Midge hot on her heels, keeping very close. Trembling, she told him what had happened and was insistent that they pack up and go home. Derek did all he could to comfort her. He said he did not want this to ruin their first trip in the camper van. They had waited so long to achieve this. They had had no holidays in ages in order to save for the van. When he had calmed her a little, he said that perhaps it wasn't a ghost after all. The girl might have got into a car and driven off. There were so many people visiting the forest. Her car could have been somewhere out of sight. He said why didn't they go to the nearest pub and get a brandy and soda, and then see how she felt?

Patricia insisted that she had definitely seen a ghost. She knew the 'feeling' of it. She had seen one before, hadn't she? But she saw the pleading look on her husband's face. It was true that they had not had a break for several years. And this was their first outing in the camper; he was so proud of that van. So she gave in. But she didn't want to stay in this part of the forest. She would opt for the pub, and the brandy and soda though.

Soon they were in the warmth and light of the pub, with Midge on Derek's knee, as all three of them sat by the cheering open fire. Patricia sipped at her brandy, her hand still shaking a little as she held her glass. A group of tourists was in the bar, laughing noisily. A few of the locals were sitting around the tables in the lounge. With tall glasses of frothy, amber beer before them, they were chatting about the poor harvest due to the wet weather and about the price of an animal at market. A very old man sat on the settle the other side of the fire to where they were sitting. 'Your missus looks a bit on the pale side,' he commented to Derek.

Patricia shifted uncomfortably. 'You come from around here obviously,' she said to the old man.

'Been 'ere all me life,' he replied, his wrinkled hands, with their discoloured thick nails, gripping his beer mug.

Patricia described where they had just parked up, and asked him if he knew the area. He said that he knew it well; he had always worked in the forest. Derek was frowning at Patricia. She knew that he was worried that she might divulge what had just happened to her. Derek was uncomfortable with these things.

'There's a story about that place,' said the old man. His blue rheumy old eyes twinkled as he looked at Patricia. It was like he knew she had seen something there.

'There is?' Patricia was leaning forwards in her seat. Derek kept very still and quiet, nervously stroking Midge.

'Yes,' continued the old man, 'there were a gypsy encampment thereabouts. Came every year at the very same time, they did. They are a peculiar kind of people they are. But the men did work 'ard. They often worked on the land. Some of the women told fortunes. And they'd all go strawberry pickin', men an' women. They used to steal the 'osses too, so some say, but I don't know 'bout that.

'Some of the women was right beauties, too. That's how young Ronnie Baines got into trouble, back in the twenties. He were a scallywag that one. It were reckoned that he liked to poach the deer. But I don't know. He always did have a few bob about 'im. I know that. Young women certainly liked 'im. He could run like that thur whippet. And he were as strong as an ox. Bold an' handsome he were. No wonder the young women liked 'im!

'Anyway, he goes and starts courting a young gypsy girl. Now that is askin' fer trouble! Gypsies won't have that. No, a gypsy must court another gypsy. He weren't no gypsy, not Ronnie. They called 'im a *gaugie*, or some such name, meaning he weren't gypsy. They don't like the gaugies around their women. An' this young gypsy girl were a pretty little piece of it, so Ronnie wouldn't stay away, despite her father and her brother telling Ronnie they would lynch 'im.

'Well, soon it were too late. The girl was carryin' Ronnie's child. Or so they say. Anyway, the upshot of it were that Ronnie, scared what might happen, disappears for a while. Well, the young girl, she falls ill after Ronnie leaves, and she dies. Some reckon she pined away. Others say she had the tubercular.

'They buried her just where you was today. They did that them days. There is many a gypsy grave in the forest. Some 'ave said that 'er spirit can't rest. Some say they 'ave seen 'er wraith wanderin' about where she used to meet up wi' Ronnie. An' you know, an old gypsy woman once tol' me that she were in disgrace wi' her people. They never put a thorn on her grave because of it. You see, when a gypsy dies and is buried, they puts a rose bush maybe, with the thorn still on, or maybe some hawthorn saplin' to grow on the grave. That stops the spirit walkin'. But no one did it for that young gypsy girl. She was cursed for disgracing her people.'

4

A Mysterious Passenger

In the 1970s Travis Deacon was often a passenger on the Winchester to Brockenhurst line. He had been forced into early retirement from his teaching at a Catholic all boys' school near Winchester, as he suffered – now quite badly – with rheumatoid arthritis.

His very elderly mother had become quite infirm, but she had not lost her stubborn streak and refused to leave the old family home in Brockenhurst, where they had lived since Travis was a child. So a nurse visited every day and social workers called, and a home help did the chores. But this meant that Travis, who was a confirmed bachelor, had to travel from Winchester, where he lived, to visit the old lady three times weekly. This she insisted upon, despite his arthritis. Guilt drove him on.

He could still drive his little old baby Austin perfectly well but he preferred to take the train. He liked the journey. He could sit with a coffee, or better still, on occasion, a double G and T, a good book, and relax as the countryside whizzed by. Sometimes, in pensive mood, he would just sit and look at the fields, trees, moorland, ponies and cattle as he passed them. Though more often he liked to study quietly the passengers who shared the carriage with him. Travis was quite a people watcher. He observed, rather than conversed.

Travis had no interest in making friends. He was a solitary man and happy to be so. His best ever companion was Mr Snookes – a rather fat, self-satisfied looking tabby cat that chose to share his small house with him.

One rather foggy autumn October day, Travis boarded the train for his usual visit to his mother. He was, however, a little peeved at having to go out at all. His arthritis was playing him up more than usual; it was the damp weather that did it. And, to cap it, Mr Snookes had been most indignant at being left with no heating on in the house. He had stared at Travis with malevolence in his bright yellow eyes, then had simply gone to ground in the warmest place in the house – the airing cupboard.

Travis had followed him, and was annoyed to find that he had curled up on the clean towels, leaving fine fluffy cat hair all over them. Mr Snookes knew all too well Travis's little foibles. And one of them was his exclamations of disgust at the cat hair sticking to his wet face as he used the towel to dry it. Mr Snookes had always been expert at revenge. Travis had to give him that.

It was in this mood that Travis made his way to his usual seat in the train, only to find, to his annoyance, that it was already occupied! Travis stared at the man sitting in what he had come to think of as his seat, with all the malice that Mr Snookes had taught him in his look.

What an extraordinary character this man was! He was dressed in a pair of rather dirty and well-worn country breeches, a pair of worn hobnail boots, that had never seen the polish tin, and a grimy shirt, over which sat an even grimier jacket. A greasy cloth cap sat on his head. His face was weather-beaten, red about the jowls, and wrinkled with age. His chin was covered in white stubble and a few wisps of straggling white hair peeped out from under the cap. His eyes were red ringed, and a watery blue. He neither looked at Travis, nor spoke.

Travis was most indignant. Even his best Mr Snookes' stare had not worked! It usually did; and to such good effect. He wondered how such a disgustingly dirty person could have been allowed to board the train. He was surely an offence to his fellow travellers? And for this foul old man to be sitting in his, Travis's, very seat, well, it was an insult!

No one else entered the carriage; the train set off, and Travis, ignoring the other passenger, pretended to read. He really had no intention of having anything to do with this old man who looked, and probably smelled, like a tramp. He shuddered, his fastidious nature making the interloper into a sort of odious fascination. The old man just sat, staring before him, as if there was no one else in the carriage.

Travis decided to concentrate on his book. Soon he found the train nearing his stop. He began to pack away his book into his travel bag. It was then he noticed that the old man was no longer in the carriage with him. Travis blinked his eyes; he must have dozed off. He hadn't slept well the previous night, yes, that was it. He must have closed his eyes for a bit, with the gentle rocking of the train. The old man must have left the carriage then.

Travis quite forgot about the encounter until two weeks later. It was a dark, dank day. The train back to Winchester had been slightly late. Travis was cold and he was irked. His mother had been quite bothersome today. His arthritis was bad, what with the weather and having to wait about in the cold. Now all that he wanted to do was to get back home, make a big pot of tea, and share some hot buttery crumpets with Mr Snookes.

When the train finally arrived, Travis went to go to his usual seat, glad at last to sit in the warm. But, to his horror and disgust, the polluted old man was already there – and in the same drab and dirty clothing.

Travis sighed with annoyance and decided that this time he would not share the carriage with this grimy fellow passenger. So he went to another carriage, and almost wished he had not, for it was rather full. He was forced to sit next to a well-dressed, middle-aged lady who for some reason smelled of bergamot oil. As soon as he sat down, she began to chatter at him in the most mundane way. She obviously loved the sound of her own voice and, even if he'd had the inclination, it would have been impossible to converse, as he would not have got a word in edgeways. She twittered happily on, oblivious, hardly taking a breath.

After about five minutes of this, Travis, who really could stand no more, got up, gallantly raised his rather fine trilby to the chattering lady, and asked to be excused. He looked furtively around for another space to sit. There was none.

There was nothing for it but to go back to where the rather appalling hobnail-booted, dirty little old man held court. Sitting, as he was, in the very seat that belonged to Travis. So Travis went into the carriage and sat down opposite him. The old man did not acknowledge his presence and Travis was almost grateful. Travis decided to ignore him completely, and drew out *The Times* from his travel bag and began reading.

Soon the odious allure was working again and Travis began to peep at the foul old man from the corner of his eyes. The offender sat absolutely motionless. He neither turned his head to look out of the window, nor at Travis. He did not read. Nor did he seem to wish in any way to converse. He just sat staring straight ahead. His expression was that of one with a mission to be completed – a journey on a train from A to B. That was all.

Travis almost warmed to him. This old man cared nothing for conversation or anything else much, by the look of him. Not sorrowful or brooding, just self-contained. Travis nearly felt an admiration for him. In fact, he might have decided to speak to him, were it not for the fact that he looked too much like a rather grubby sort of Fagin.

It was then that Travis noticed something else. There, next to the old man on the seat, was an oily hessian bag. Travis stared with a sort of cold dreadfulness at the bag; he had an uncomfortable feeling that it somehow held a life of its own. There was a sensation of such discomfort when he looked at it, which started deep down in the pit of Travis's stomach, that he hardly dared to ignore it. He could not keep his eyes from it. The bag moved of its own accord, on occasion. And it moved in such a way that set Travis's nerves jangling.

The old man sat still as a rock, arms folded, looking straight ahead. The bag was moving as if there was something alive inside. Travis felt the hairs go up on the back of his neck; his skin began to creep. A fine perspiration wetted his brow. He felt he ought to run for his life but he couldn't move a muscle. He was transfixed with fear.

Travis did not know how long he sat thus. But suddenly he let out a scream. It was an involuntary sound. He just stood up and screamed at the top of his voice. The tension had become too much. Then he suddenly found his legs, rushed over and pulled the train's emergency cord.

Soon, many startled people crowded into the carriage. He hurriedly told them about the old man and his bag. Whatever it was in that bag was dangerous, of that he was sure. Someone ought to see to it! Those gathered there looked at him with astonishment. Soon they were all shuffling out. He heard comments as they left. Loony was a word he heard, madman another.

The well-dressed, middle-aged lady was standing in the doorway. 'There is no one else in this carriage, my dear,' she said in a patronising voice. 'It is empty, save for you. If I were you, I would go and see your doctor. You have probably been overdoing it.'

When Travis stepped down from the train at Winchester, he could still feel his face burning up as he remembered the comments from his fellow passengers. Also, he remembered keenly the telling off he had had about pulling the emergency cord for a non-emergency, as if he were some aged schoolboy who liked a malicious practical joke. Some people had avoided him completely as he stepped from the train. He could see by their faces that they obviously deemed him quite mad.

It was as he was just about to hail a taxi to escape from all of this that a small man, dressed in the uniform of the railway, approached him from out of the gloom. He looked around in a conspiratorial sort of manner, before speaking. He said that what Travis had seen was a ghost. There was an old man that used to travel on the train from the New Forest to London, every now and then. He was a real old countryman, the sort that could hunt, kill, or catch any living creature. And this old man would gather adders from the New Forest, and take them to a medical establishment in London, where they would be milked for their venom, for research and anti-venom. The old man would be paid good money for them. This was, of course, years ago. But a few people had seen the ghost of the old man and his snakes. People who worked on the rail knew all about the story though they were not encouraged to talk of it. It might put the passengers off!

Travis was more than glad to get home that evening. He shut the door on the world, made the tea and buttered the crumpets. And, as he said to Mr Snookes, who was now comfortably curled up on his lap after sharing the crumpets, it really might be time to get the baby Austin out again, and stop using the trains.

5

The Devil's Hands

Marie Crosby was a tiny woman but her friends all declared that she had the personality of a gander! Her father owned a small farm on the Hampshire/Berkshire border. Marie had been an only child, so she got stuck into the farm work as good as any boy or man, and helped her parents in their sometimes hard toil.

After her parents had died, she sold up the farm and took early retirement in Gosport. She bought a small house that needed little tending to, with only a courtyard garden. It was heaven not to have to go out in all weathers and to stay in bed a little longer in the mornings – and even have the indulgence of being allowed to be ill now and then.

Marie loved to socialise, after all those years of loneliness on the farm, with just her elderly parents for company. She now had a nice, healthy little bank balance, and really didn't need to work but she liked to take a job here and there. Her favourite was working behind the bar in a pub, so as to meet as many people as possible. She served behind the bar in several different pubs in Gosport over the years, and enjoyed every minute of it. It was in one of these pubs that she met Denny Scouter.

Soon she and Denny became firm friends. The relationship blossomed into something more but Marie refused to marry Denny, although he had asked her several times. She was naturally flattered by his asking. And it wasn't that they were incompatible. She felt sure she loved him, and he her. But she did not want to lose her independence. That is what she told him. That was what she felt.

She used to worry Denny all of the time, with this independence of hers. He would drive to see her in Gosport, then she would drive to

Stubbington to see him, where he had a small, but pretty cottage of his own. It was her driving to see him that worried Denny the most. He hated the thought of her on the road at night alone. What if she were to break down? She would often be leaving his house at midnight, or the wee hours, to drive home, all alone, to Gosport.

Denny frequently expressed his concern to Marie but she would only laugh. She would say that she was afraid of nothing and could handle herself perfectly well in nearly all circumstances. After all, if she could lead out a bull to the field, and face out an over maternal cow with her calf at foot, then she could do almost anything! Denny was still not convinced. Besides, he had heard some strange tales about the Stubbington to Gosport road …

When Denny mentioned this, Marie had roared with laughter. Superstitious old wives' tales, she would say, all made up, just to entertain the gullible. She had lived a long time out in the middle of nowhere, on the farm. She had never been afraid of the dark. In fact she had never had any reason to fear anything. And, as for spooks and suchlike, that was nonsense! She had never come across such things in her life and did not intend to!

Denny wished he could agree with her but he could not. He had had a couple of strange experiences in his own life that could not be explained, except by putting them down to some supernatural happening. His brother and his mother had experienced such things too. He was convinced these things existed. It was something that he and Marie would have to agree to disagree about.

Marie would listen with a wry smile when he related his experiences. She knew that he was a man of integrity, but she felt that he *believed* in such things; she did not. She thought that Denny was the sort of man who might not look for logical explanations; rather he might look for supernatural ones. He was naturally religious and had a wonderful imagination. He was creative, carving beautiful things out of stone. He was most sought after by the church to replace broken gargoyles, angels and Madonnas.

One night, in the winter of 1993, Denny and Marie had had a really good evening out with friends who lived near to Denny. He had had a beer or two, but Marie had kept to soft drinks as she was driving. It was a frosty night so Marie insisted that she must go back to her own home to check that all was well as the heating wasn't on. Denny begged Marie to stay overnight, as she often did, but she was having none of it. She said that she must go home. She would be perfectly all right driving home alone. She'd done it hundreds of times by now.

So, to Denny's annoyance and acute anxiety, Marie set off in her little car. It was a dark night. The wind had got up a little, throwing sleet and some hail into the windscreen as she drove. The wind came in little gusts, and the few leaves that were now left to fall from the trees whirled before the headlamps, ghostly images in the lights. A pale sickle moon hung in the sky, obscured now and then by black racing clouds. A moody sky, her father would have called it. And that was what it was; a moody sky. Marie gave a little shiver and turned her car heater on. She was dressed for an evening out, not the winter winds.

She put on the radio, something she rarely did, but tonight she felt that she needed a little company. Why, she could not tell. It was alien to her to feel this way. She chided herself. Had she been listening too much to Denny's stories?

Then suddenly, as she turned onto the Stubbington road, a small branch crashed against the windscreen, obviously having fallen from a tree. It made her start in her seat. Then, after the initial shock, she burst out laughing. 'You silly old kook,' she said, out loud to herself. 'You are spooking yourself up!'

She turned up the radio a little louder and laughed some more. For goodness sake, it was Denny telling their friends his ghostly stories tonight. They had lapped them up. They were a weird bunch! Never mind, the evening had been entertaining. Marie put her foot down a bit harder on the accelerator. She had a notion to get back home quickly tonight. Odd really, she almost felt a little nervous. It was not at all like her.

She kept her eyes on the road. She didn't want any more falling branches hitting the windscreen and there might be debris in the road. She could not stop shivering, despite the heater being on. She wished that she was wearing her coat. It was in the boot. Never mind, it would warm up soon. But it didn't warm up. It got very much colder in the car, to her dismay.

Then, on the periphery of her vision, she caught sight of something that caused her to scream. Yes, she actually screamed. And, in the moment that her eyes left the road to look at the thing in her car that had petrified her, her concentration failed and, before she knew it, she had swerved and was off the road. Then everything just went black.

She woke up in a hospital bed. A rather pretty young nurse was soon telling her that she had been brought in after a road accident. She had been knocked out. Her head had probably hit the windscreen. She would need a scan to see if everything was all right but she was doing fine. It was now best that she just rested. It had obviously been a shock. They had given her an injection to calm her and help her to sleep.

The next day she awoke to find Denny sitting next to her bed. She was up and into his arms immediately. To his distress, she was sobbing and shaking. He thought that it must be the shock of the accident. He had never seen her like this before. He could hardly believe that his strong-minded Marie could get quite so upset about a minor accident. He had been told that no one else had been involved and that she was quite unhurt, except for a bruised forehead.

He held her close until she had stopped sobbing. Then she turned to him, looking up into his face earnestly. 'Denny, do you know why I swerved?'

'No, love,' he replied. 'Why did you?' He felt very concerned now, looking into her unusually pale face and seeing the evident fear in her hazel eyes.

She swallowed hard and seemed to be fighting for words. Then she said, 'There were these hands, right on top of the passenger seat next to me, as though they belonged to some invisible fiend sitting in the back seat.'

Denny's eyes grew wide. 'What on earth …?'

'I don't know what they were, Denny.' Her mouth had gone dry with the fear of remembering. 'But they were huge hands. They were covered in black hair. And … and they had huge long claws. Not nails, Denny. Claws! You might say they looked like the Devil's hands!'

6

Fairies at the Rufus Stone

Nigel was a rather handsome young man, twenty years of age. Perhaps handsome is the wrong word. Nigel was beautiful. He was beautiful in the sense that Michelangelo's *David* is beautiful, or the statue of the fallen Lucifer in the Cathedral of St Paul in Leige, Belgium is beautiful. In other words, he had the look of an angel. He had a kind of doe-eyed poet's appearance, dark hair flowing to his collar, long lashes and very pale, flawless skin. He had a generous mouth, full of very even little white teeth and a perfect, straight nose. It was almost a girl's face, but with just enough masculinity to have females of all ages staring after him in a breathless manner. He was very tall and slim, and with a hint of mischief about him that was beguiling to all who met him. He was also unfailingly generous and kind.

Despite these wonderful attributes, however, and his great popularity with most people, Nigel was an unhappy young man. The source of most of this unhappiness was that his father found him such a great disappointment.

Nigel's father, Angus, was a successful merchant banker. He had sorely wanted Nigel to follow in his footsteps, as he had followed in his father's footsteps before him. But Nigel had no interest whatsoever in his family's business, and even less aptitude for it. His brother Peter, who was only seventeen, showed much more inclination towards the banking world. So, eventually, Nigel was looked upon by his family as being somewhat of a failure, much to his great distress.

Nigel's father also liked to go hunting, which he did with gusto, as did Peter. But Nigel had no stomach for it, and found himself sympathising with the fox, always hoping the poor thing would escape.

Riding he liked, horses he loved, but hunting he hated. This was another thorn piercing his father's side – another great disappointment to the family.

Just lately, when Angus was in his cups, he would unkindly say that Nigel didn't seem like any son of his. In fact, perhaps he was not his son at all. And this was said in earshot of Nigel. And then Nigel would remember back to being in the nursery with nanny, and how she would sit him on her knee and say, 'Nigel you are a changeling child. I really think you are! You are far too pretty, and have the look of an elf about you.' She never said this harshly, and always kissed his forehead afterwards. But it made him despondent now to think of it. The truth was, he never did feel that he was part of his family at all.

On top of all this, Nigel was failing miserably at university. Since he was refusing to go into merchant banking, Angus had decided that he must go into the law. His uncle, Angus's brother, had a highly respected law firm in the City. Nigel was expected to join it but he did not want to. However, because he did not know what it was that he *did* want to do, he couldn't argue against his father's wishes. But this again only led to more failure.

One thing that always did cheer up Nigel was when the family went down from London to stay at the small farm his father had purchased near Cadnam. Nigel loved the New Forest. He had little interest in the actual farm. He thought it unkind to keep animals to eat, and was a vegetarian. He also thought that crops ought to only be grown organically. This viewpoint only caused further trouble and ended up with his father calling him a New Age wimp.

But Nigel loved to wander in the forest. He would spend hours walking in it. He was mesmerised by light and colour. The forest was a paintbox of natural light and colour so stunning that it would leave Nigel dazed and drunk with the delight of it. He could only really be himself when he was alone amongst Nature. Then he would feel his soul fly free. He found himself just smiling at everything: a grasshopper, beige brown on the back, lime green underneath, its huge great eyes like some sort of alien; a leaf, half skeletal, twirling on the mercurial surface of a clear, cool stream; a fern, delicate, just unfurled, shaking in the soft summer breeze; a rabbit, dewy eyed, standing on its hind legs and washing its fine sparkling whiskers; the sunlight, dappling his own legs; the burgundy brown earth of the forest floor; a robin, red-breasted, bright-eyed, singing like an angel. Nigel never tired of it! How he was in love with it, so very much in love with it all.

One day, Nigel had come down from London to stay at the farm with his family. He was feeling at a particularly low ebb. He had been doing so badly at his studies that his tutors had told him that maybe it was time to give up. He had had to tell his father, who was absolutely livid with anger. Angus had said some very hurtful things and made it clear that he thought his son a waster. He also told Nigel that from now on his allowance would be stopped.

Nigel was quite distraught. He felt a complete failure. What was he to do? He could think of nothing he was good at. And now he had no money either.

Nigel got into his car and drove out to the eastern side of the forest. He stopped in the car park near the Rufus Stone. He sat there miserably for a while, feeling too dejected to get out. But it was a lovely day in early spring. There was a pale clear light to the blue sky and the young sun was just beginning to feel warm. Only two other cars were parked along with his, the still chill wind keeping most of the tourists at bay.

Despite himself, Nigel felt his spirits lift to be in the forest again, away from classrooms and the noise of London. He got out of the car and walked to find the Rufus Stone. He'd seen it many times before, and he laughed to himself as he looked at it. Of course, there was no stone, just three iron plaques describing how a king had been accidentally killed on this spot, whilst hunting in the forest. He remembered how, on his first visit, he had expected to see some sort of huge and magical stone, like the ones at Avebury and Stonehenge. He wondered how many other people had thought that too?

Nigel's mood was improving as he walked out amongst the trees. He knew the area very well and felt quite at home. The tender buds, a brilliant green, were nestling against the browns and russets of the knobbly branches. The air held all the expectancy of spring, and something else ...

The 'something else' he could not quite grasp. It was as though some kind of powerful static electricity hung in the air. He felt the hairs rise on his arms and on the back of his neck. It made him tingle.

Soon he was quite deep into the forest. The air was zinging. Everything around him became accentuated. He remembered reading about someone who had taken the hallucinogenic drug mescaline; he imagined this was how it would feel. It was a sensory overload, the sensuality of Nature; the forest. The sights, the sounds, the scents, the sunlight so clear, as sharp as a sword – he had never felt so truly alive.

Then he saw *her* coming towards him. She was riding a milk white horse. He could hear the sound of many tiny bells, then realised there were hundreds of little silver bells plaited in the horse's mane. And such a horse! He had seen many fine horses, but this one was of majestic elegance, the like of which he had never before seen. Arched of neck, wide of nostril, liquid of eye, and delicate of ear. It moved with a graceful rhythm that pronounced perfect conformation.

The rider was not alone. There were others behind her, all mounted too. But they melted back into the trees and disappeared out of sight. Only she came on towards him, astride her horse, at a gentle walk. Then, she slipped easily from the saddle, leaving the horse grazing in the glade.

She was as tall and slim as he was, her lissom walk fluid and effortless, covering the ground with ease as she approached him. She was dressed all in velvet green; a long flowing gown, covered with a red cloak of fine-spun wool, held together by a silver clasp. Her hair flowed to the waist, the colour of a wren's back. Her eyes sea green, and slightly tip-tilted, the lashes thick and dark, the eyebrows arched. Her mouth was the shape of a rosebud. He had never beheld such beauty. He thought she must be the Queen of Heaven.

He was too spellbound to say one word. And she too said nothing. She walked right up to him and laid slender arms around his neck; he could smell the scent of meadowsweet and broom. Then she kissed his lips.

As she did so, Nigel thought for one moment that his spirit had left his body. He was floating above himself, looking down at her arms still around his neck, her lips still on his. Then, he heard her voice in his head, like the tinkling of a stream. The kiss was over; she stood back. She was speaking in his head; her lips did not move.

'Soon you will know your way. Your sadness will leave you. Know that you are loved. Your loving has not gone unnoticed amongst my people.'

She looked deeply into his eyes. He thought that he might drown in hers. He saw waterfalls, streams and rivers, and then the ocean, in the depths of those green eyes. She touched his face with a white hand as delicate as a lily. Brushing his cheeks, then his lips and chin, she turned and walked away.

Astride her horse again, she was gone. He wanted to call after her, but he could not find his voice. He came over quite faint and had to sit down. He was in a stupor. He ached for her to return but somehow knew that she would not. Soon he was driving home. He could hardly believe what had happened. How could this be? What was it all about? And yet, somehow inside, deep inside, he knew.

In the weeks that followed, Nigel gave up his place at university. He rented a cottage on the edge of the New Forest. He began to paint. He had no training in art but this did not deter him, and soon he was busy at the canvas. Picture after picture emerged. It seemed to flow from somewhere inside of him, down his fingers and out through the brush. It thrilled and frightened Nigel to see his own talent. The pictures were all amazing pieces of art that were as good as any master's.

They were all of Nature and mainly of the forest: trees, moors, ponies, hills and streams, all wild and beautiful. Eventually people from all over the world wanted them; they were in great demand.

One day, he suddenly found that he had painted *her* and her horse. Then he painted her people. These canvases he kept to himself. When friends saw them, they took their breath away. He knew it was *her* that had awakened his talent. He would never forget that day in the forest. Often, he would go to his diary and look at the page for 21st March 2004. It said 'Today I saw fairies.'

7

Sweet Fanny Adams

In the summer of 1982 Fenella Shaw and her husband Ross were invited to the christening of Fenella's friend Michelle's baby girl. The christening was to be held at the pretty church at Alton, where Michelle now lived. This was Michelle's first baby, so it was to be quite an event for both family and friends.

Therefore, Fenella and Ross, dressed in their very best, travelled from Lymington, where they lived, to go to Alton church for the christening. It was a delightful Sunday in June, the summer sky bright blue and cloudless, the fields a soft green, shimmering in the heat. The smell of new mown grass and roses met Ross and Fenella as they alighted from their car.

People were already entering the church, although it would be a good twenty minutes before the start of the service. It was a colourful event, with everyone turned out like so many peacocks in their finery. Fenella and Ross followed suit, and entered the cool, sweet darkness of the church. After their rather warm and sticky journey, they were glad of a respite from the sun. There was a smell of old hymn books, beeswax and flowers all mixed into a heady scent.

It was a little while after they had been ushered to their seats that Fenella noticed that a bit of the hem of her pretty, white daisy-embroidered cotton dress had come down. Mortified, she whispered to her husband, 'Darling, a bit of my hem has only gone and come down.' Ross looked at it, frowning. 'Fenella it really isn't that noticeable. Forget it!'

Fenella felt her cheeks burn. 'Ross! Only a man would say that! I have a little mending kit in the glove compartment of the car. I'll just go and sew it up.' Ross sighed. 'You can't go now. You might miss the service.' Fenella was resolute, though. 'No I won't. There is enough time. I can't possibly leave it like this, I'll be too conscious of it.'

And so Fenella got up and went out of the church, leaving her husband sitting staring down at his hymn book. She made straight for the car, found her kit, and did the sewing needed. She smiled to herself after finishing her handiwork and patted her dress. 'That's better,' she said aloud.

Nearly everyone had gone into the church by now as she locked the car. Then, as she started back for the church herself, something caught her eye. There was a little girl all alone in a nearby field. She seemed to be about eight or nine years old, with long dark hair and a skirt that reached nearly to her ankles. Her appearance was a little old-fashioned, in fact. The poor little thing seemed very agitated; she ran up and down the edge of the field, she looked like she might be crying. She was obviously distressed.

Fenella felt distressed herself, just watching her. She tried calling out, asking if she was all right. But the child either took no notice or, in her anguish, did not hear her. Just then a couple of late arrivals for the christening passed Fenella, nodding and saying hello, distracting her for a moment as they did so. When she looked again the little girl had disappeared. She must have gone through a gateway or something. Fenella thought it might be best if she walked down the road just to check that the girl was all right.

But then Ross came out, a little flustered, 'Come on, for goodness sake!' he said, taking hold of her arm. 'The service is about to start!' Fenella wanted to protest. But what could she do? She had to attend the service, how could she let her friend down? So back in the church she went and sat through the service. But she couldn't stop fidgeting. Her mind wasn't on it at all. She could not enjoy it. All she could think about was the little girl, and how distressed she had seemed; it was playing on her mind.

Ross noticed her mood and, on the way to the christening tea, which was to be held at a local hotel, he asked her what was wrong. She told him about it. They had seen no sign of the little girl as they had left the church.

Ross said, 'I expect she had lost a ball or something, Fen. You know what kids are like. They make a drama out of things like that, it worries them.' But Fenella was adamant. 'No, Ross, she looked far too upset for that. Oh God, I do hope that she is all right. There are so many weirdos about. Do you think we should inform the police?'

'Fen, for goodness sake,' said Ross, alarmed. 'I mean. Just what have we to tell the police?' 'I don't know. Just tell them what I saw and ask them to check it out.' Fenella burst into tears.

Ross pulled over. He hugged his wife. 'Hey now, hey now,' he said, kissing her. 'Calm down. We'll go to the police if that is what you want. But I can't help thinking it's only something like the little girl has lost her dog out on a walk or something. This is a pretty rural place. I shouldn't think that many bad things happen here. Here's a tissue, love. Look, maybe we ought to go for the christening tea and then if you still want to we'll go to the police? What about that?'

Fenella nodded reluctantly, and dried her eyes with the tissue. Soon they were inside the hotel. Fenella cheered up a little. The toast to parents and baby done, they moved into the vast dining room where the buffet and drinks had been laid out. The food looked wonderful and there was a glass of champagne for everyone.

Fenella still felt a little shaky, though. So with trembling hands she took her plate and glass, and found a quiet corner to sit. Ross decided it best that he remained social and began to go around chatting to some of the other guests. As Fenella nibbled at a smoked salmon and watercress sandwich, cut beautifully into tiny squares, without the crust, she was aware that someone was pulling out a chair and sitting next to her. She looked up to see a rather stout elderly lady, with very bright violet eyes staring back at her.

'Hello. I'm Doreen. Great Aunt of the little one.' She had a glass of pale sherry in one hand, and a cheese scone on a plate in the other. Fenella smiled back as best she could. Really the last thing she had wanted was company. She still felt upset about the little girl. It was almost odd how it played on her mind so. All that she had seen was a child in tears. Children were always fretting over things, weren't they? Ross was probably right. There could be nothing to it. She wished she could rid her mind of it.

'I saw you when you came in,' said the old lady, her head cocked like a crafty jackdaw. 'I saw you and thought, well there, we are birds of a feather me and that girl!' Fenella smiled uncertainly, not knowing how to reply. Thinking that perhaps this lady might be the eccentric of the family, she said nothing, but nervously took a sip of her champagne.

Doreen put her hand lightly on Fenella's knee. 'I mean,' she said, with emphasis, leaning forward and looking directly into Fenella's eyes, 'that you, like me, have the sight.' Fenella started as though an electric shock had gone through her. 'The sight?'

'Yes,' replied the old lady kindly, 'the sight. I am a spiritualist. A medium, you know.'

Fenella felt more than uneasy now. She looked across at Ross. She wished he would come over and she could ask to leave but Ross wasn't looking her way. He was in deep conversation with an elegant grey-haired man in a well-cut, dark brown suit.

'Don't let the things you see ever trouble you, my dear,' said Doreen, as if she were talking about today's shopping list. 'It used to trouble me at first. Then dear Mr Senning at the spiritualist church taught me how you are able to switch on, or switch off, at will.'

'Please,' said Fenella, who was now quite alarmed, 'I really don't know what you are talking about.' 'But my dear,' insisted the old lady, 'that little girl you saw today …' She put down her sherry glass, and her half finished scone. She sat staring at Fenella knowingly with her deep violet eyes.

Fenella went dizzy for a second. She felt that this strange little old woman could see inside her mind. It was irrational. She couldn't speak but held her fingers to her mouth. 'My spirits told me,' said Doreen in a convincing voice. 'They are never wrong.'

Fenella rubbed her own brow, and then made a fist and put it to her lips. She must get up from this chair, go and find Ross and leave this bizarre old lady to it. This was frightening her. But it was as if she were frozen. She could not move.

'My spirits told me that you saw her in a field outside the church today, is that correct?' Doreen looked unflinchingly into Fenella's eyes, waiting for her reply. Fenella found her voice at last. 'Yes,' she whispered. Doreen blinked and gave a look of concern. 'Oh my dear!' she dabbed her lips quickly with a serviette. 'You will have seen poor little Fanny Adams.'

Fenella felt very near to tears again now. She stared incredulously at the old woman. She wanted her to continue but she also very much did not want her to continue.

'How very distressing for you,' Doreen patted her arm in consolation. 'Poor dear Fanny was murdered, you know.'

Now Fenella was quite sure that she had heard enough. She felt sick. She slowly rose from her chair and went to find her husband. The old lady was obviously quite mad. But somehow she had known that Fenella had seen the little girl that afternoon. Doreen just stared after her as she left, she did not try to follow.

Fenella excused herself from the christening party, saying that she felt unwell. She managed to get Ross to leave there and then. She looked back and saw Doreen staring after her, with those vivid violet eyes. She couldn't get those eyes out of her head all of the way home. She could not bring herself to tell Ross what the old woman had said. But how on earth could Doreen have known what she had seen?

For weeks, Fenella had dreams about the little girl she had seen that day. And of Doreen, with her violet eyes. Then, one rainy Saturday afternoon when Ross had gone to play rugby, she phoned her friend Michelle and asked about Doreen. She also asked her friend if she had ever heard of anyone called Fanny Adams.

'Oh, Fanny Adams. Did Aunty Doreen tell you about her? Her grave is here, in the churchyard, at Alton. It is a well-known story in these parts. It's quite famous for it, in fact. It's a rather macabre story. Fanny was murdered as a child. She was murdered and dismembered. Horrific!' Fenella went cold.

'It happened years ago, of course, in the late 19th century, I think. But some people say they have seen her ghost, you know. And, horribly, the sailors used to use the term "sweet Fanny Adams" to describe the meat they were being served up, meaning no animal meat in it. How awful is that?' Michelle laughed nervously at the black humour of it. Fenella was feeling quite faint. She ended the conversation with her friend, pretending that a visitor had arrived.

Some weeks after this, Fenella decided to visit a spiritualist church. She found sympathetic ears there as to her experience of seeing Fanny Adams. Soon she was training in mediumship with them. Fenella went on to become a medium of renown. Doreen had been quite right after all.

8

The Car

On a dark winter's night in 1993, Murry Steele and her friend Carol Berkley were driving along in Murry's little metallic Citroën, heading for Cadnam. They both lived in Ringwood, but were travelling that evening to stay with friends who were having an anniversary party the next day.

Murry and Carol were excited at the prospect. They were going to prepare the food for the guests and help get things ready for the party. Murry was renowned for her cooking, and her ability to be creative with party ideas. So both women were in high spirits, chattering gaily about what was being planned for the celebration.

It was a typical damp November night. The last few leaves dropping from the trees looked like huge golden moths swirling in the car headlamps. The forest road they were on had very little traffic; it was 7 pm and already very dark. It was a moonless night, and visibility was mainly down to the road immediately ahead. Murry kept her eyes well on the road, as it was not uncommon for some type of wildlife to run across in front of you; a deer maybe, or a badger or fox, and sometimes a pony. The two women were quite used to this as they had both lived in the New Forest area all their lives.

After a few miles, Murry noticed a set of headlights in her rear view mirror; it was obviously another vehicle, it was almost tailgating. When Murry commented on it, Carol said that maybe it was someone who didn't really know the road too well, and that they were using Murry's car to guide them. Murry just wished that they would overtake, or hold back a bit, to give a proper stopping distance. It was inconsiderate of them! The headlights kept dazzling her in her mirror.

But the two ladies forgot the annoyance and continued a merry conversation. Carol was describing the cake she had made for the anniversary, and how they were lucky to have it with them to take, as her collie dog, Mojo, had nearly managed to filch it from the kitchen table before they left.

Then, suddenly, Carol complained of feeling cold. Murry checked the car heater, only to find that it was not working. She felt rather annoyed, as she had only had the car serviced two weeks previously. It started to rain, not heavily, but gusts of wind sent the rain splattering onto the windscreen. Murry put on the windscreen wipers. In the rear view mirror she saw that the vehicle behind was still on their tail. It was a black car, large and rather wide. It might be a limousine but, of course, she could not see its length.

She started to feel very irritated at its doggedly close proximity. She and Carol decided that it was probably a limousine, possibly one of those posh actors, or TV presenters who had weekend cottages in the forest. They always believed that they had precedence on the roads. Murry thought that most of them suffered from far too big an ego; she had come across their arrogance before. Carol said that some of them were nice enough but Murry said that they belonged in the city, not the countryside. Especially if they kept going around doing what this one was doing, hogging the road, getting too close, as if it didn't matter because they had a flashy limo!

It was then that the windscreen wipers stopped working. Now Murry was fuming. Hadn't she just paid good money in the garage to have her car serviced? Visibility was now so poor that she decided that it might be best to pull over and see if she could fix the wipers. Perhaps something was stuck under them? The wind could have thrown a twig on the windscreen. She looked into her mirrors as she pulled over. Well, at least that car behind was a little way back now, not up her backside any more, thank goodness!

Murry got her coat from the back seat, pulled it on and popped on her headscarf. As she straightened up outside the car, a skirmish of rain hit her face and hands. There was nothing untoward on the windscreen. The wipers ought to be working. She got back into the car and turned the key in the ignition, only to find that now it would not start. Murry was far too angry to feel uneasy but Carol felt jittery, though she had no idea why.

Then the inside of the car was illuminated, telling them that someone had pulled in behind them. Carol craned her neck to see that it was the black limousine. She breathed a sigh of relief. At least help was at hand! She did not fancy a walk to the nearest telephone, a trudge of several miles along a dark and lonely forest road.

Murry kept trying to get the engine to turn over. She really didn't want to ask for help. Carol begged her friend to go to the car behind and ask for assistance. Murry ignored her, tried the engine again, and then found out that the whole car seemed to have gone dead. Nothing now was working, including the lights.

Carol sighed as Murry was trying everything all over again. She pulled on her suede jacket. The rain had ceased for now and the clouds had blown away to reveal a navy sky with bright, bright stars. She was shivering as she approached the limousine, her head bent against the chill wind. She looked through squinted eyes into the interior of the big black car. She saw plush black leather seats but no driver. She made her way alongside the length of the vehicle. Then she stopped, put a hand to her chest, as if in surprise, and ran back to her friend.

It was a little while before Carol could speak at all. When she could, she breathlessly reported that the black limo was not a limo at all, it was a hearse! And, not only that, it had a coffin in the back. She said there was no sign of the driver.

Murry told her to calm down. So what if it was a hearse? Murry had seen them many times at funerals; she used to live next to a churchyard. As for the driver, he probably had been caught short. He'd be back soon. Then he could give them some assistance with the car or perhaps take one of them to the nearest telephone.

It was at this moment that the hearse drove off. Carol let out a little exclamation. Murry swore, gritted her teeth and tried the ignition again. This was more in exasperation than hope. But to her surprise the engine turned over and the lights came on. Murry shrugged her shoulders. Carol was astounded. At last they were away again!

Murry, relieved, began to chat gaily away again. But Carol, almost crouched in her seat, saw headlights in the wing mirror and her fear began to rise. She told Murry that the hearse was following them again. Murry said that she must be mistaken. The hearse had passed them as they were parked, no way could it now be behind them again! But, when she checked her mirror, sure enough, there it was. The hearse was certainly following them again. Carol became quite hysterical and Murry found that her hands were slipping on the steering wheel; they were covered in perspiration. She put her foot down on the accelerator. She was now doing 65 mph. The hearse speeded up too, cruising easily behind them. She went faster. So did the hearse. By now they were going far too fast for the forest road.

Murry would not give up. She pursed her lips. No idiot hearse driver was going to terrify her! She stepped up the speed a little more. Carol began to scream now. She was telling Murry to stop it, or they'd have an accident for sure. But try as she might, Murry could not get rid of the hearse. It stayed on their tail. Carol was still shouting for her to slow down. She said she thought she might be going to be sick. Murry slowed down. She began to pull over, bumping over uneven ground. As they ground to a halt, Carol got out of the car and promptly threw up. Murry sat where she was, pale and shaken.

Carol got back in and both women looked fearfully behind but there was no sign of the hearse. The road was empty and quiet, the leaves still swirling down around them. A fox crossed the road just in front of them, an indistinct figure that shrank back into the shadows of the forest. The hearse had not passed them. Where had it gone?

Soon they continued onto their destination. Neither spoke. Both felt that the hearse had been hounding them. Perhaps hounding them to their death? Murry, who was never a reckless driver, had been so, with the big black car behind. And Murry's car? How come everything had packed up, then miraculously started? It was all too weird! They had both lost their heads and they knew it.

In the years that followed, neither woman forgot the terrifying experience. They told a few friends about it. The word got around. And to this day some folk are still anxious about travelling that road at night.

9

The Young Pilot

In the 1980s a young flight lieutenant, whom we shall call Colin, was at a dinner being given by the famous Red Arrows. It was a hilarious and fun evening and Colin, who was a first-time guest, had enjoyed it immensely.

When the meal was finished, the banter had stopped, and the shots of brandy and port had been dealt out, a few stories started to be told around the table. Some of these stories were inevitably about the Second World War and the heroic actions of the comrades of the older men who were present.

Colin was listening intently, marvelling at some of the tales. He really wished he had been born early enough to have experienced such things! But he also knew what a precarious time it had been for the young airmen, half of whom had not had the time to be properly trained before going into action in the air. Many had been shot down by the enemy, of course, never to return. They had been lambs to the slaughter.

After the evening was at an end, one of his friends, another airman, gave him a lift home. Douglas, his friend, commented to Colin on what a wonderful evening they had just had. Some of the anecdotes had made him roar with laughter. He also said how impressed he had been by the stories of the wartime heroes. He asked Colin if he had any stories to tell, as if he wished that he could prolong the evening's enjoyment.

Colin looked a little embarrassed, 'Well, I don't know any wonderful stories like those wartime ones,' he said.

'No, obviously not. You are far too young!' laughed Douglas.

They fell silent for about the next mile of the drive before Colin carefully cleared his throat and then said, 'I do have a rather strange story though.'

'Go on,' said his friend.

'Well, I certainly wouldn't have wanted to have told this one in front of all those men tonight!' said Colin. 'They might have thought I was barmy.'

Douglas did not reply. He was intrigued. He didn't look at Colin, but kept his eyes firmly on the road, waiting for him to begin. Colin cleared his throat again, 'It was a cold night. There was a full moon. The sky was perfectly clear. The stars were sharp and bright, and one could see the constellations easily, the Plough, the Great Bear, and the rest. The moonlight was such that it seemed like a very pale kind of day. I was doing the night round at Farnborough, accompanied by the orderly sergeant. I was a new recruit then, learning everything. Part of our duties was to check that the airfield buildings were secure.'

Colin stopped here, swallowing hard, as if it were difficult for him to continue.

'Yes?' Douglas had turned to his friend, trying to encourage him to continue.

Colin licked his lips nervously, 'Whilst we were walking amongst some of the buildings that face the runway ... I ... I thought I caught sight of somebody who should not have been there. An intruder.'

Colin stopped again. He was now wringing his hands. Douglas could tell by the look on his face that there was something that he was finding very difficult to talk about, something that frightened him.

'I ... I told the orderly sergeant that I thought that we had an unwelcome visitor. He told me to be on my guard and that we must check it out. People are not allowed to wander about the airfield, especially at night, as you well know, Douglas.'

'Of course not!' replied Douglas, now really quite excited by his friend's story.

'So we went on towards the buildings,' continued Colin. 'We could see everything as plain as day in the moonlight. There is a kind of eerie feel to the whole place at night at the best of times. The buildings look black and sinister, you know, like dark crouching beasts. And everything had this unearthly look in the pallid light of the moon. Anyway ...'

Douglas, his interest truly captured now, waited with baited breath. He just wished that Colin would get on with the story!

'Anyway,' Colin took a deep breath, 'when the sergeant and I got to the buildings I saw *him*. It … it was an airman in full Second World War flying kit. He was walking right towards us! He had on a chest-type parachute harness, over an orange life jacket. There was no parachute pack attached though. He was also carrying a canvas holdall. He was very young. Quite a handsome young man, high cheekbones. Blond. Well built. He did not look at the sergeant, or me. The sergeant walked forwards as if he were going to apprehend him. It was just then that he disappeared. Just sort of dissolved, right before our eyes!'

Douglas's hands tightened on the steering wheel. He felt the hairs rise on his neck.

'So, Colin, what you are telling me is that you and the orderly sergeant both saw what would be called an apparition?'

'Yes, we did,' replied Colin emphatically. 'But afterwards he refused to speak of it. In fact, when I told someone else about it and called the sergeant over to verify what I had said, he categorically denied it. That made me look a right fool. Since then I don't like to tell anyone about it. But I knew that you would believe me, Douglas.'

'That sergeant was probably very afraid of what he'd seen, Colin. It was probably better for him if he denied it. It is a very strange thing to witness. And you both saw it. That is unusual.

But, yes, I do believe you all right.'

'Yes,' said Colin, 'I knew that you would. I think those stories tonight about the war heroes brought it back to me. I have tried to forget the whole thing. It made me feel so weird inside for a long time after it happened. I couldn't help but understand how afraid all those poor young men must have felt, going to certain death in their aircraft. But how courageous they all were as well, going anyway. When I saw *him* – the – the ghost, that did more for me than any remembrance service could, Douglas. God bless them all. I truly hope they all went to a place where they found peace and happiness.'

10

The Girl

Perry Maslin was used to driving along Hulbert Road towards Waterlooville. This was because his girlfriend Sandra lived nearby. Perry, who was 21 years of age, would finish work at the building site, go home to his parents' house, take a shower, watch a bit of television, have a bite to eat and then set out for Sandra's flat at around 7 pm every evening.

Sandra, who was a hairdresser, would finish work at around five, or on late nights, Thursday and Friday, eight, and go back to the little flat she had bought, and of which she was very proud, to wait for Perry. She very much hoped that soon she and Perry would be married, and that he would move in with her for good.

Perry hardly ever missed an evening with Sandra, unless he was unwell. He occasionally went out with his mates, but not very often, as Sandra thoroughly disapproved. She knew what young men got up to together when off out on their own.

So, when one dark evening in January 2007 Perry had not arrived by 7.30 pm, Sandra was worried. She tried ringing him on his mobile but, to her concern, it was switched off. Perhaps he was still driving? He always switched it off when driving. She then rang his parents' house. They declared that Perry had set off at his usual time. They were sure that he would be there soon.

Sandra decided that Perry had probably gone to the supermarket to get some beers. Knowing him, he had bumped into a mate and was chatting about football. Yes, that was probably it all right, Perry could waste hours talking football! She went over and switched on the television to settle down and watch a soap. First though she went into the tiny kitchen and made a cup of instant coffee.

But, when she went back into the sitting room, she could not settle. She felt uneasy. She tried Perry's number again. It was engaged. She frowned. Then, her mobile rang. She could see it was Perry; he must have been calling her, when she tried to call him.

'Perry, it's you!'

'Yes, Sandy, it's me.'

'Where are you? Is everything all right?'

'I'm on Hulbert Road.'

'What? How come you aren't here by now?'

'I've been looking for a girl.'

'You what?' Sandra' s voice had become shrill.

'Sandra, you don't understand!'

'No, I don't think that I do.' Sandra's voice had become ice now.

'I gave this really pretty girl a lift. And …'

'Perry, I think you'd better not say any more. If you don't come over here this minute everything between us is off!' She pressed END CALL.

Her mobile rang again. But she would not answer. How dare he call her, telling her that he had given some pretty girl a lift! She was fuming.

Soon Perry arrived. Sandra was sitting on the sofa, arms and legs crossed, her face vexed. Perry knew that when she sat in this way it meant trouble but tonight he was too disturbed to care. Sandra, noticing how white and strained he looked, unfroze a little.

'You don't look well. Are you okay?' she asked, still a little reluctantly.

'The weirdest thing has happened!' Perry sank down on the sofa next to his girlfriend. 'You got a drink of anything here?'

'Only the sweet sherry I keep here for when Gran comes round.'

'That'll do,' said Perry, rubbing his eyes, and shaking his head in a kind of mystified way.

Sandra got the sherry and shoved it into his hand. 'Well?' she asked, with hands on hips, legs planted firmly on the floor, as if to say, this had better be good. 'What's this all about?'

'I … I don't know what to say,' ventured Perry. 'It's all so odd …'

'Try starting at the beginning,' Sandra's voice was cold, she clipped out the words.

'Well ... I was on my way here ... it's very cold and wet out there ... I saw this girl walking along the road on her own in the dark. She was tall, with a short skirt, long boots ...'

'No wonder you noticed her then!' broke in Sandra sarcastically.

'Shut it, Sandy. This is no joke. I was just going to drive on by but, as I was about to pass her, I caught a glimpse of just how young she was. I would say she was about sixteen at a guess. Sixteen, and all alone on that dark road! I mean anything could happen. So I pulled over for her to catch up and I was going to offer her a lift ...'

'You fool!' shouted Sandra. 'She could have got you into no end of trouble! Some girls make a habit of it.' She turned to look incredulously at her boyfriend. 'Oh my God! That's it, isn't it Perry? She hasn't gone and accused you of something has she?'

'NO, Sandra. That isn't it. Stop jumping to conclusions.'

'What then?' Sandra folded her arms again, she was more than angry now.

'Calm down, Sandy. And listen,' said Perry, who then continued with his story. 'She came up to the car, so I got out and asked if she was going to Waterlooville. Before I even asked if she wanted a lift she had got into the back of the car. I noticed in the mirror that she was very pretty. She had long dark hair in a high pony tail, dark eyes, and a very pale face.'

'Oh, yes, you would notice that, wouldn't you? I really can't believe you are telling me all of this, Perry, I really can't.' Sandra sat with her arms gripped tightly around her, looking with disbelief at her boyfriend. Perry was about to tell her to shut up again, but he saw that now anger was brimming over into tears, and so he decided against it. Instead, he gently said, 'Sandra, just listen until I have finished, please.'

It was the way that he said it that silenced Sandra. He had even used her full name, he only did that when things were serious. So she sat meekly and waited for him to continue.

'Anyway, she got into the back of the car. And I noticed a funny thing. Despite the rain she did not look at all wet. In fact her hair and her clothes looked perfectly dry! Another strange thing is that I felt really, really cold all of a sudden. I actually began to shiver as I started the car. My head went all swimmy, too. For a few minutes, I thought I might be ill or something. Anyway, I drove off. Sandy, I couldn't have gone a few hundred yards when I noticed in the rear view mirror that she was gone! The back seat was now empty!'

Sandra stared at Perry. Her eyes were now like saucers. 'She had jumped out of the car you mean?'

'No, she couldn't have done. I didn't hear the back door open. I stopped immediately I noticed she was gone. There wasn't any time for her to have hidden anywhere and what would be the point anyway? She was just nowhere to be seen ...'

Sandra was dead silent for a few minutes. Then she said, 'Oh my God, Perry, I think that you have seen a ghost!'

Then she went on to explain that several times over her time at the salon she had heard stories similar to Perry's about Hulbert Road. They had been spoken of like dangerous secrets, by some of the local clients.

Sandra and Perry just sat staring at each other in a kind of disbelief. But really they had no doubts whatsoever in their minds that the girl Perry had given a lift to ... had indeed been a ghost.

11

The Haunted Cottage

It was the summer of 1979. Louisa Chalcott, her husband Ken, and their three children were moving into a farm cottage near Fareham in Hampshire. Both were native to Somerset, but Ken had lost his job due to the farm he was working on folding up. So now they were moving to a new job for Ken and a new home for them all, a tied cottage, as was usual for farm workers. They were rather relieved at Ken getting another position at last. He had breezed through the initial interview, Ken was a man with much farm experience, and he had looked at the accommodation himself to save dragging the kids around. He had raved about it, saying how lucky they were to have a detached cottage in such pretty countryside. There was plenty of room for the kids to play and a big garden for Louisa to tend – Louisa loved gardening.

When Louisa first set eyes on the cottage, she did not like it one bit. But how was she to express this? How ungrateful it would seem. Ken had been through months of worry, unable at first to find a job with accommodation that would be suitable for the whole family. Then this came up and she could see how the clouds had lifted from him. He looked less strained, and happy at last that he had found work again and somewhere to live. So Louisa said nothing, despite the fact that she could not stop a shudder running through her, as she turned from the boot of the car, her arms full of boxes, and looked at the cottage.

To all intents and purposes it was pretty – grey flint stone walls, a neat little slated roof and oblong mullioned windows. But the windows looked like sinister dark eyes to Louisa, staring belligerently back at her. The front door, painted a hideous green, with patches of paint peeling, was slightly ajar, showing a strip of blackness that looked eerily unwelcoming.

Then a ray of sunlight came out from behind the clouds and illuminated the whole cottage. It then took on a different face and looked quite appealing and benign. Louisa put down the boxes and relaxed her shoulders. She let out a sigh of relief. She was getting fanciful. She had a habit of it. She must not upset Ken and the children with her nonsense. The place just needed a lick of paint. She was sure that once their familiar things were in, it would become much more homely.

Soon everyone was inside. Ken got the kettle on so that they could have a longed-for cuppa. Louisa searched through the boxes to find some mugs. The three children, a little boy and two girls, ran around, glad to stretch their legs after the car journey. Louisa had a look around whilst Ken was making them all tea. The carpets were clean, but a trifle shabby. In the kitchen, on the floor, were old Marley tiles in black and white but in surprisingly good condition and there was an aged gas cooker that was reasonably clean and still worked. The kitchen cupboards were well worn and in need of replacement.

The décor all over the cottage was dark and rather sombre, and did nothing to dispel a certain heaviness in the atmosphere. The staircase would have been charming, had it not lacked light, being made of solid oak. The upstairs had a wonderful view of the surrounding countryside and would be light and airy, if the décor was changed to something more cheerful. Louisa immediately decided that redecoration of the house was a first priority.

Ken was calling for them to come and have the cuppa he had made, and he had already set up a small table in the sitting room to put the tray on. Louisa came downstairs and joined him, to find Poppy, their eldest, already there with her father. Leo, the youngest, was running around in the garden, his blond head bobbing by, below the windowsill. Ken was opening a packet of mini Bakewells, one of which Poppy quickly stuffed into her mouth.

It was then that a shrill scream came from the kitchen, causing Louisa to throw down her cake and slop her tea. She ran in to find Lisa, the middle daughter, who was seven, sprawled on the kitchen tiles, crying. Louisa quickly picked her up and checked her over. As far as she could see, no harm had come to her, except for a bruised knee. She picked the little girl up in her arms and brought her back into the sitting room, with the promise of comfort in the shape of a Bakewell tart.

But Lisa would not be comforted. 'Someone tripped me up, Mummy!' her mouth was a pout, tears still in her eyes.

Ken laughed and her sister Poppy giggled along with her father. 'Don't be a silly willy, Lisa,' said Ken. 'You were the only person out there in the kitchen!'

'No I wasn't neither,' replied Lisa, peeved. 'An old man came in and tripped me up! He did it on purpose too.' She turned to look at her mother. 'He isn't going to live here with us, is he Mummy?' She looked really concerned.

Louisa went cold. Her face blanched. She had a feeling of great foreboding. She was inclined to believe what her daughter had just said. Ken saw his wife's face. He walked over and lightly laid a hand on her shoulder. 'Come on, Lou, Lisa has a colourful imagination. She always has had. She's like you. And she loves telling stories. Remember the make-believe friend she used to have that no one could ever see?'

Lisa had stomped off out into the garden to join her brother, but not before saying, 'I did see that old man too! It is not a story.'

Louisa was feeling quite sick but she forced a smile at her husband. She knew just how much getting this job meant to him. And the security of having a home again, when it had looked as if they'd be on the streets. It had nearly killed him with the worry of it all. The relief at finding somewhere had been immense. How could she possibly tell him what she really felt about the cottage? And now all this with Lisa! There was no way she was going to say anything further so she just replied, 'Yes, Lisa really is such a fanciful little girl.'

The first night that the family moved in went quietly. Everyone was exhausted from the move and went to bed early, collapsing under the covers to sleep deeply. It was Saturday and Ken was to start work on Monday.

The next day Louisa took the girls off to Fareham to buy some paint to decorate the house. She was feeling more optimistic. She was sure that once the cottage had been spruced up, it would feel a lot more cheerful. It would surely dispel the darkness and feeling of foreboding that it seemed to hold. Ken stayed at home, washing down the walls and woodwork, ready for the decorating. Leo, who was always a handful to take shopping, stayed at home with his father. He was playing in the garden and also running in and out of both the open front and back doors, with boundless energy.

Ken was washing down the paintwork in the kitchen when he heard little Leo let out a loud squeal and then he began to cry. The boy came running into his father, tears streaming down his chubby little face; he was holding his arm.

'Oh dear!' said Ken, picking him up. 'What have you gone and done little man? Fell over have you?'

Leo's face puckered. 'Man did it.' He held out his arm to his father; a nasty small round bruise was appearing on his plump little white forearm. Ken frowned. He went outside. No one was around. 'You catch it on the gate, son?' he asked the little boy. Ken knew Leo's vocabulary to be limited due to his age. He wanted to be sure just what the child was saying.

'Nasty man,' sobbed Leo, putting his arms around his father's neck.

Then it clicked for Ken. Leo had been listening too much to his sister. The little boy idolised Lisa, and followed her around everywhere; he copied everything that she did. He shook his head to himself and sighed. Lisa and her stories! Now she had Leo at it too. Ken put the boy down, went to the first aid box, and smoothed some 'magic cream' on Leo's arm. This was what Louisa always did for a bruise. It was Arnica cream, but the children saw it as 'magic cream'. They always had some put on and were soon satisfied that all would be better. It soon worked for Leo and off he ran; Ken saw him through the window, in the garden, playing with his lorries.

When Louisa and the girls came home, Ken did not mention the incident. He thought it best not to. He didn't want to start Lisa off again. And he could see that his wife was jittery about the place.

They spent the day decorating, working hard. Poppy made them cups of tea, and kept an eye on Leo. Lisa washed down walls, and ran with paintbrushes and rollers where needed. Everyone felt in high spirits and there was much laughter, despite the hard work. Very soon the sitting room had bright white gloss paint on the doors and skirting boards, and the walls were a cheerful primrose yellow. It certainly made a difference. Louisa started to relax and feel happier.

At 6.30 pm Louisa took Leo upstairs to the bathroom for his bath. Lisa was already there, diligently filling his baby bath, which Leo still insisted on using. She was pouring in Baby Bubbles, and the water was warm, foamy and a bright blue. The bathroom had the best décor in the house as yet. A previous tenant had made it quite inviting. The walls were cream, and there was a clean pink bathroom waterproof carpet on the floor. The tiling around the bath had *Punch*-type caricatures, depicting the nonsense rhymes of Edward Lear.

Louisa undressed Leo, tested the water with the inside of her wrist, and lifted him into the bath. He splashed about in the water, sending it everywhere. He was too big really for the baby bath. He was crowing with laughter as Lisa got his bath sponge, in the shape of a fish, and started to wash him. He threw water in his sister's face. Then Louisa noticed the bruise. 'Oh dear, you been falling over, Leo?'

Leo's face suddenly clouded. His lips pouted. He stopped playing in the water. 'Nasty man,' he said.

Lisa looked at her little brother horrified. ' Leo,' she said, with great concern, 'did nasty man have big, bushy, grey eyebrows?' She pointed to her own eyebrows, trying to explain. Leo nodded and looked as though tears were not far away.

Louisa stood up. Her nerves were wrought. 'Stop it!' she cried out. 'Stop this at once! Leo doesn't know what big bushy eyebrows mean! Stop encouraging him, Lisa. You will frighten him.'

'He does know too!' Lisa's face was stone. 'Leo is much cleverer than you think.'

Louisa put fingers to her lips and swallowed hard. She was trembling and her heart was pounding. 'I said stop this nonsense!'

'Not nonsense.' Lisa was adamant, her brow corrugated, lips pursed. 'Now he's gone and hurt Leo too.' Louisa was wiping away a tear. 'Please stop it, Lisa,' her voice had gone gentle now. 'Don't let Daddy hear you. You know how hard it has been for us all. Daddy has found us this lovely place to live. We should all be grateful. You will like it when you settle down. There's even a riding school not far away. I'll get you booked in for some lessons, how is that?'

Lisa just stared back at her mother stonily. 'I don't want to stay here,' she said, 'that old man frightens me.'

Louisa was on tenterhooks all that evening. She tried watching television with Poppy and Ken, but could not concentrate. Lisa's words had upset her. More to the point, they seemed to back up her own feelings about the cottage. Leo had gone to bed. Lisa too had gone to the bedroom she shared with her little brother, after much persuasion and a promise that she could keep a lamp on all night long.

At 12.15 that night Louisa and Ken were abruptly awoken by their youngest daughter's screams, quickly followed by Leo howling at the top of his voice. Poppy came rushing out of her room and followed her parents towards the bedroom where Lisa and Leo were. Ken lifted the door latch with what he found were trembling fingers. Poppy and Louisa were right behind him. Inside the room Lisa was sitting on her bed in hysterics. Leo was in his cot still howling in sympathy with his sister.

'For goodness sake! What on earth has happened?' asked their father.

Louisa ran over and picked up Leo. Poppy went and put her arm around her sister. 'It was him,' sobbed Lisa. 'He kept on poking me with his finger until I took notice. He sat on my bed.'

'Who was?' Ken was startled; he was still half asleep.

'The old man. He's horrible. He doesn't like us. Big bushy eyebrows. And such eyes!' Lisa was crying again.

Louisa said nothing. She was comforting Leo. But her heart was thumping and she felt quite sick. 'You've gone and woken your brother,' was all that she could say.

Ken went over and took Lisa up, and put her on his knee. He kissed her forehead. 'Sounds to me like you've had a bad dream, love. Settle down now. It is just a dream. That's all.'

'I couldn't have had a dream, Daddy. I haven't been to sleep! I've been reading,' replied Lisa.

He was rocking her back and forth as if she were a baby. 'Dear, dear, reading until this time of night! You must have dozed off, honey pie. Dreams can seem so very real. Especially when you've got such a magnificent imagination as my little girl,' her father said, soothingly.

Lisa closed her eyes for a moment in resignation. Her father was not going to believe her. Poppy sat silently on her bed, white-faced. Lisa looked at her, seeing that her sister believed her.

Louisa said that perhaps all the children could come and sleep in their room just for tonight, after all this upset. Ken agreed. Leo was put between them in their bed. Poppy and Lisa shared a mattress on the floor. Ken whispered across to his trembling wife, 'A bad dream, love. Moving is always upsetting, especially for children. After all, they're having to start at a new school, leaving behind all their friends. I do know it must be tough for them. No wonder there are nightmares, eh?'

Over the next few days Louisa and Ken worked hard, and the cottage looked brighter and more homely, with the new décor and their familiar things inside. Louisa had chosen all bright and lively colours, for both walls and curtains. The gloom of the place seemed to dispel, leaving only a few sinister dark corners.

Ken had started his new job. And one morning, it being the girls' summer holidays, they accompanied their father to go and feed the calves. Poppy, particularly, liked to do this – putting her fingers deep into the bucket of warm milk, getting the calves to suck them first, before they could be persuaded to stick their heads in the bucket and suck up the milk for themselves. She loved their dewy brown eyes with the long lashes, and the cold, wide, wet noses that nuzzled at her hands.

After her husband and the girls had left, Louisa went out into the garden to hang out the washing, it being a bright cloudless day, with a warm breeze. Leo was out in the garden too, astride his toy tractor, reproducing engine noises that set his lips aquiver with the effort. Louisa looked around at the garden. It had been sadly neglected. A few straggly rosebushes were in flower, but the flowers were sickly. A clump of wallflowers had survived and thrived. Ken had cut the lawns, but they had gone a bit brown with lack of rain. The rest of the garden was mainly weeds. There were masses of convolvulus, the myriad of white flowers raising their wicked heads to the sun; the plants had a rather poisonous and putrid, rank smell.

Louisa decided that she might set about clearing some of the weeds, but she wanted a cup of tea first. So she went into the kitchen, leaving Leo happily playing on his tractor. She made the tea, then went to the fridge for the milk, humming a little song to herself as she did so. Then she heard a crash behind her. She turned around. The mug was on the floor, hot liquid streaming from it all over the Marley tiles. She went very pale and with trembling hands picked up the pieces and mopped up the tea. She knew for sure that she had put the mug well onto the worktop, as was her wont, used as she was to having small children around. A feeling of horror crept over Louisa that she was hardly able to contain.

But when Ken and the girls came home at lunchtime, she said nothing of any of this. In the last few days everyone's spirits had risen. Even Lisa seemed more settled. This was not the time to rock the boat. The girls were chatting gaily about their morning. Ken was commenting that he had a cow soon to calve down. She was showing all of the signs. He had put her into the calving pens. He had a feeling that she might go into labour quite soon.

The day passed with no other mishaps but Louisa was still jumpy and she had a feeling of foreboding, despite her best efforts to be cheerful. She kept herself busy to stop her mind wandering, and very soon it was time for the usual bedlam of bathtime and bedtime for Leo. Ken said that he must go back to his cow; she was very imminent now. Louisa really did not want him to go but knew that he must. Anyway, it would be ridiculous, almost childish, to ask that he stay, without solid reason. Besides, she did not want to alarm the girls.

Poppy and Lisa begged to stay up to watch a film on television. Louisa consented, more than glad of the company. So Ken left them to it, saying that he didn't quite know how long he'd be. Cows can be reasonably fast, or sometimes slow to birth, just like any other creature.

At 10.30 pm, just as the last of the light was fading outside, they all heard a faint tapping at the window of the sitting room. Poppy went very quiet and stared, horrified, at the closed curtains. Lisa screamed and burst into tears. Louisa, breathing hard and wishing that the telephone had been connected by now, got up from her chair and said, 'Calm down, you two! It's probably just a bat or a bird late home to roost.'

'You know it's not that, Mummy,' said Poppy, getting up and switching off the TV. She sat on the sofa with her sister, both of them staring at their mother with frightened eyes.

Louisa was trembling all over, despite herself. She felt her nerves were at breaking point. She ran over and snatched back the curtains. The girls came right over behind her as she did so. What they had all dreaded to see met their eyes.

An old man's face was pushed against the window, staring fiercely at them. His hair was pure white, longish, windswept over a craggy reddened face, which was weathered like a piece of hewn granite. His huge bushy white eyebrows, sheltering vicious bright blue eyes, conveyed a look of true hatred and malice. His fist was raised; he was shaking it at them. They just stood there, for what seemed like an aeon, too frozen with fear to move or make a sound.

'It's *him*!' whispered Lisa, getting back her voice at last. 'It's the *old man*. He hates us. He wants us out of here!'

'Ohhhh, Mummy!' screamed Poppy. 'Lisa is right. I knew that she was right all along!'

Louisa, now able at last to move, ran to the door to see if the bolts were along. They were. She knew this really, anyway, as she always locked all the doors when Ken was not with them at night. Poppy and Lisa had their arms about each other. 'It's no good locking the doors,' said Poppy, 'that won't keep him out.'

An icy hand of fear had gripped Louisa. She remembered that Leo's top bedroom window was ajar and instinctively ran up the stairs to shut it.

She was no more than halfway up when she heard both girls let out shrill screams. She ran back down and found them in the kitchen. They were staring, with total horror, at the old man who was now standing by the kitchen table glaring at them with those awful eyes. Louisa could see that the bolts on the back door were firmly shut.

He looked absolutely solid and real. But then there was a sound as of the rushing of wind, and the figure melted into thin air before their eyes. Louisa heard another scream, and realised that it had issued from her own mouth. Mother and two daughters clung together and sobbed. They were trembling uncontrollably.

When Ken came home that night, he found his whole family crammed into Leo's room. The girls were sitting saucer-eyed and silent. Louisa held a now sleeping Leo protectively in her arms. He took one look at them all, and knew that living in the place was not going to work.

It was the day that they were moving out that a new postman pulled up at the gate. 'Oh dear, you off? Hmm. People never do stay 'ere long.'

'Is that right?' asked Ken. He was piling some of their belongings into the car. He had never seen the apparition his family had experienced, but he had never before witnessed such intense fear in them. It was enough to make him take another job elsewhere.

'Oh yeah,' continued the postman, 'folks round 'ere say this place is haunted.'

Ken looked up. Louisa was stood at the gate, gazing at the postman.

'Old bloke that lived 'ere about ten years back got pensioned off from the farm. He had to get out. He didn't want to move. Worked here a long time. Farmer said he had no option. He needed the house for a new worker. He never did move out tho'. He died in there. Hung himself.'

12

The Mistletoe Bough

In the early summer of 1963 Suzette, a petite and pretty strawberry blonde, got engaged to Rodney, a tall and rather handsome young police officer.

Rodney had been sent to Bramshill House to do some of his training. Bramshill is a magnificent Jacobean mansion set in lovely gardens in the countryside near Hartley Witney. It was taken over in 1953 by the Home Office to be used as a police training college.

Rodney took Suzette for a drive one day and showed her Bramshill House from afar. She was immediately besotted and begged Rodney to ask if she could be allowed to see a little of the inside of the house and walk in the beautiful grounds. Rodney knew that this request might be difficult to arrange as Bramshill was not open to the general public. However, he was so totally infatuated with his girlfriend that he could not bear even to think of that tiny freckled little nose wrinkling slightly, the sign that Suzette was upset. So Rodney pleaded and persuaded, and eventually got permission for Suzette to visit the house, see the first floors and walk in the gardens.

And, oh, how glad was Rodney that he had achieved his loved one's wish, when he saw Suzette walking towards him, as he stood on the drive of Bramshill House that bright day in May! She looked vibrant in the sunshine. She had on a little Mary Quant mini dress in a large floral pattern, with an 'o'- shaped chain belt around her tiny waist. A big, pink, floppy-felt hippy hat covered her glorious hair, keeping the sun from her delicate complexion.

She waved and smiled that special smile, the one reserved for him. He felt that his heart might burst with pride at the thought that this amazing creature had agreed to be his wife in exactly one year and a day. He must be the most fortunate man in the world. What a stunning bride she would make!

Soon they were inside the house. Suzette enchanted all the people that she met. She gasped at the magnificence of the place and raved about the flooring, the furniture, the art, the panelled walls. She commented how lucky the young men were that came here for training. She expressed how she would love to live in the house and how sad it was that it was not a family home any more. Rodney, watching her, got so much pleasure from her enthusiasm. She was such a precious jewel!

That Bramshill House had a more sinister side, Rodney refrained from telling his fiancée. Suzette had no clue of its history, not being a local girl. Rodney had heard strange tales since he had been stationed at the house. However, he did not think such matters belonged to such a sun-drenched day and the prettiest girl in the world.

'Oh Rodney, what an amazing place!' said Suzette as they stepped back outside and into the sunshine. 'To think I only saw a little of it. It is vast really. One could play hide and seek and never be found!' Her little tinkling laugh echoed in the gardens.

Rodney suddenly shivered at her words. It was as if a big black cloud had come and blotted out the sun.

'Mind you,' she continued, 'the place also has an odd kind of feel to it … I suppose that is probably not unusual. These old places have an extraordinary aura about them, don't they?'

'Yes, yes, they do.' Rodney tried to shake off the uneasy feeling; he could not explain it to her anyway.

Suzette reached up and kissed him, 'I know you have to go back in to your studies. I'll just go for a stroll around the gardens before leaving, that's okay, isn't it?'

Rodney smiled; he was feeling more cheerful again. 'Yes darling, you go. The gardens are so very pretty, you'll love them. I will be out to see you off in about half an hour or so if they'll let me, which I expect they will.'

Suzette smiled back, and, carrying her hat in her hand, walked off. The sun played on her hair as she went, turning it into a kind of spun red-gold. She found the lovely old gardens a pleasure to walk in; the trees were magnificent. She looked back at the house itself. It was impressive, as one might expect for a one-time country seat of aristocracy. Bramshill, or then, Bromeselle, had even been mentioned in the Domesday Book. The place was steeped in history but it looked to her as if it might also hold morbid secrets within its ancient walls – a place of sadness, though she could not think why.

After examining the different flowers and shrubs, and admiring the well-kept lawns for a while, Suzette suddenly felt a little light-headed. She thought it might be the heat. She had foolishly left her hat off, and the sun was quite fierce considering it was only May. She found a bench in a quiet shady spot and sat down.

Her eyes dropped and she began to feel drowsy. She rubbed them with her index finger and pressed lightly between her eyes. She blinked; her vision was a bit blurred.

When she closed her eyes, it was snowing. Soft flakes fell silently around her. Everything had a gentle covering of snow. It was very cold. The earth was crisp beneath her feet. It was daytime but it was a dark winter's day and she could see candles lit within Bramshill House.

Suddenly she found herself back inside the house. She looked down at herself and saw that she was wearing a cream satin bridal gown that belonged to another era. Holly and mistletoe bedecked the house along with many flowers. Servants flitted here and there. A table was laid with a feast of fine food and wines. She was sitting at the table along with quite a few other people; wedding guests.

A middle-aged man and woman were presiding; they called her their beautiful daughter, the man was making a speech to the guests. There was a toast to the 'happy couple'. A man in his late fifties, dressed in breeches and long jacket, came up and kissed her cheek. His look as he did so, was lustful, which he was careful to hide. Everyone cheered. She felt somewhat bewildered and not a little repulsed.

Catching a glimpse of herself in the huge gilt mirror on the wall, she saw that she was not Suzette any longer. She was a very young girl, with long blonde hair, pretty, her slender body just showing the first signs of womanhood. In her hand there was a sprig of mistletoe. She looked across at her husband. For, yes, she had married him. Her mother had talked to her about it. It was a marriage of duty. This rather obnoxious elderly man would bring wealth to a family that was sliding into debt.

Now she would share his life and his bed. She knew that she was doing it for her family. How else would they keep their standard of living, their home, even? Tears stung her eyes. It was a heavy price to pay; too heavy perhaps …

What could she do? She would do anything to put off the nuptials. Perhaps they could play a game, she suggested, to make the day really jolly? She was such a child that she really thought that she could stall what she had dreaded these past few months.

'Oh,' she cried, 'let us play hide and seek!'

The guests all clapped. Everyone thought that it would add to the festivities. What a good idea. Who was to hide? 'I will hide!' said the girl. Everyone clapped some more. Her husband let a wolfish grin slide across his face. Ah, hunting of a different kind!

So off ran the girl. And Suzette ran with her. Was her. They ran to a part of the house that Suzette now knew did not exist any more. It was gone in modern times, demolished. The girl ran down gloomy ancient corridors, past pictures of long dead ancestors and antique tables, chairs, and chests. Her small footfalls lost in the vast high-ceilinged rooms.

Suddenly the girl stopped before a great carved oak chest, mistletoe still clutched in a delicate hand. She quickly opened the lid and, pulling up her long skirts to reveal dainty satin shod feet, hopped into the chest. It was big enough for her to lie down. She did so, pulling the lid closed after her. The lid gave out a hollow click as it shut. The girl blinked; she felt suddenly afraid. All was blackness inside.

She lay there a few minutes, a little worried. Then she giggled. Oh my! Everyone would be looking for her by now. It would take them a little while to find her. She had chosen a good place to hide, had she not? She could feel the mistletoe in her fingers. No need to be afraid. Think of something nice. Her mind began to wander.

She thought about the handsome young boy with the nut-brown hair that she often saw in church. He, like her, usually yawned all the way through the sermon. He was the son of a local squire. But, from his dress, he looked as if he had tasted London society. How she wished it was someone like him she had been wed to, instead of that grisly old man.

It had started to get quite stuffy inside the chest. She felt a little over warm. Perhaps she should push open the lid a little? She pushed hard with both hands. The lid stayed solidly shut. Now she panicked and pummelled it with her fists. The lid still did not move. Her heart began to beat wildly. She felt as if she was inside a tomb …

She swallowed hard, her face now quite flushed. She pulled herself together. Silly girl! They would all find her any minute. Of course they would! Weren't they all looking for her right now? It was hide and seek. Soon, of course, they would find her. They were playing the game at this moment, looking for her hiding place. She could pride herself on finding such a good place to hide. How ingenious she was. They would soon open up the lid and exclaim how clever she was!

After what seemed like an age, fear crept back into the darkness of the closed chest. No one had come. No voices could be heard. The airless box was beginning to be suffocating. The girl pummelled for the last time with her fists and let out a hideous scream …

Suzette opened her eyes, as if from a dream. A scream came from somewhere, and she was shocked to find that it was from her own lips. Only it sounded nothing more than a pathetic squeak, as it often does when one has just woken oneself from a dream. She was trembling uncontrollably. Tears began to run down her cheeks. How ghastly! How could she have dropped off to sleep and had a dream like that?

Rodney found her thus. She got up and clung to him as if for dear life. He was distraught, wondering what on earth had happened to her. She told him her dream. Or was it a kind of vision? She really did not know. He had to drive her home; she was not composed enough to drive herself. Rodney was shocked to find that he already knew the story, having come across it when he started his training at Bramshill House. There was no way that Suzette, however, could have been aware of it.

It was the story of the daughter of a previous owner of the house, long ago. It was just as Suzette had described it. Of course they never did find the girl, Anne, alive. She was discovered much later; in the chest, suffocated, as if she had been buried alive. She was in her bridal gown, with a sprig of mistletoe still in there with her. Her parents had been so distraught that they had had the whole wing of the house where the tragedy had occurred pulled down. But, according to some, even this drastic measure was not enough to stop poor Anne's ghost from wandering. Perhaps she was still hoping to be found?

13

The Phantom Barge

In late September 1981 Martin Bradshaw was out walking his dog, Molly. Martin's house was not far from the Basingstoke Canal and he loved to walk along the towpath. One could see plenty of wildlife and, besides, it was a perfect place to walk Molly. She could be safely let off her leash for a bit and she just adored to go splashing into the water for a swim.

Martin often took the path towards Odiham Castle, now a ruin. He seldom saw anyone else apart from the occasional dog walker, like himself, or perhaps a narrowboat but there were not yet many of these on the canal.

This suited Martin. He was a solitary man by nature, especially since his wife, Susan, had died five years back. Susan and he hadn't had any children, so when Martin retired from his job as an engineer they had moved into a small house, where Martin still now lived. It served him well enough. He was a man of few needs. After Susan's death he had found himself a little lonely, so had bought Molly, then a bundle of soft fur, puppy fat and energetic mischief. Molly kept him busy. It was she who had warded off any depression of spirits that came with the death of his wife. No matter what, Molly could always bring a smile to Martin's face.

Molly was now a full-grown, rather chunky black Labrador. She had gone, as usual, to get her lead and take it to him, which, of course, meant that it was time for a walk. Molly was a clever dog, and Martin believed that she knew every word that he said to her. So he would hold long conversations with her, about whatever he was doing.

So off they went on that September afternoon. Martin unleashed a rather over-excited Molly as they got a little way along the towpath. A gentle mist had started to gather around the canal banks. A few mallards flew up as Molly came snuffling along, trying to find a stick to carry. A coot called and, farther down the bank, a heron walked off in a stately, but furtive manner, before taking to the wing. Martin smiled as he watched the birds. He also noted that the floating pennywort was multiplying again, despite being cleared that spring. The fish had already started to become more inactive, due to the weather starting to get cooler, so he saw few of those.

The mist now had begun to thicken. He realised that visibility was down to about one hundred yards. Instinctively, Martin called Molly to him, although he could think of no real reason to worry. Not much harm could come to her on the towpath, and she could swim very well, as all retrieving dogs seem intuitively able to do. Molly reluctantly came to heel, looking askance at her master, as she was usually allowed to run on ahead regardless. Martin put up the hood of his waterproof. The fog was wetting his hair and he felt a chill envelop him.

'Shall we have some sausages for supper, Molly?' he asked. He did not know quite why, but he wanted to hear the sound of a voice, even if it was his own. There was something sinister about the change in the air. It was nothing he could put a finger on, just a feeling. A shiver went up his spine. He bent and patted the dog. It was reassuring to feel her warmth and aliveness. 'You love those sausages from the butcher's, don't you, girl?' His voice sounded somehow flat, muffled by the fog.

As they neared the pathway that turned off towards Odiham Castle, Martin thought that he heard what sounded like heavy footsteps coming from the other direction, towards him, on the towpath ahead. He stopped to listen. Molly stayed to heel behind him, tail slightly wagging, as she did when she was a little anxious. Thud. Thud. Thud. Slow, but sure footsteps. He could see nothing through the thick vapour but the sound was too heavy for human footsteps.

For goodness sake, thought Martin, surely no one would be stupid enough to ride a horse along the towpath in this weather? The path was narrow and also slippery. It would be too dangerous and there was no room really to pass pedestrians! His anger rose. How inconsiderate some people could be! He had never met anyone on the path on horseback but it definitely sounded like a horse's footfall. He expected it was one of those people who just didn't realise how treacherous the slippery banks could be. He felt slightly more comfortable with these indignant feelings than the previous ones that had started to creep up on him.

It was then that he realised that Molly was nowhere to be seen. Fear gripped him again. She must have scampered off, startled by the footfalls. He called her name again and again. He realised that there was no way she could see; the fog was getting thicker by the minute. He would have to rely on her hearing his voice. He was now glad that he had trained Molly well, and that she was an obedient, responsive dog. He was anxious to get her on the lead before the horse and rider appeared.

It was then that he turned and saw a piebald heavy horse, coming toward him. It snorted, the hot breath thick on the air from its nostrils. Oh my! What a sight! There was no rider, of course. It was a towing horse, something rarely seen on the canal in modern times. It was obviously towing a barge, which he could now see was darkly, silently, gliding on the water, rising out of the mists. He almost laughed with relief. Obviously someone was trying to do things the old ways. And why not? He would love to have a chat with them about it if he could. Such things interested him.

'Molly, come!' he shouted. 'Nothing to worry about, old lass.' His voice trailed away as he looked closer at the barge. There was something peculiar about it. It had a strange look to it. The *Mary Celeste* came to mind.

He turned again to call his dog. He knew that she could not be far. She hardly ever left his side for long. He turned again, expecting the horse to be very near now. But to his astonishment neither horse nor barge were anywhere in sight!

His heart started to pound. He broke out into a cold sweat. How could this be? He was a rational man; he searched for a rational explanation. There was none. The horse and barge had simply disappeared! It was then that it dawned on him just what he had witnessed. He began to run homeward, frantically calling for his dog as he went. Oh, God! Molly, come on! He almost feared for her. What on earth was going on? The thick fog was relentless, veiling everything in his path.

He found Molly, at last, huddled and cowering by the stile that led home. She was overwhelmed to see him, jumping up, trying to lick his face. He quickly put on her lead and she virtually dragged him all the way home as if the demons of hell were on her tail.

When they eventually got home, Martin rushed to lock the door behind them. Molly ran into the kitchen, as soon as he'd unleashed her. She didn't wait to be dried as she usually did; instead she crouched against the radiator and shivered. Her eyes were full of fear and reproach. Martin could not coax her away, even for her favourite digestive biscuit. He found himself trembling too. He made a hot mug of tea and added some whisky. He felt in a state of shock.

For days afterwards Molly would not go for a walk and certainly not along the towpath. Martin, too, found it hard to regain his nerve to walk that way. There would always remain a feeling of dread that went with what he had witnessed on the banks of the Basingstoke Canal.

14

Strange Phenomena at the Army Grave

In the 1950s Bob was enlisted into National Service, as were lots of young men of his age. He became a dog handler and was based in Aldershot. One night, whilst in a local pub with some of his friends, sitting around the open fire, he told them a strange story:

'There were quite a number of us dog handlers at Aldershot in the '50's, everyone loved it actually, working with the dogs. The job entailed taking it in turns to walk the perimeter of the camp with the dogs each night, on guard. There was a small railway that ran around the camp, for moving heavy freight. Well, one cold winter's night, an army lorry was hit by this train; it had eleven of the boys on board. It was terrible. Every one of them died in the accident. Everyone was so shocked. No one could really believe such a tragedy could happen on so small a railway set-up. They could not help thinking how it could have been any of them there that it could have happened to. They all had been in the lorries themselves and crossed the same crossing where it happened. It really did shake up everyone.

It really was awful, so many young lives lost. It was all in the newspapers at the time and people from all over the place were sending their condolences. These lads were mates of all who worked there, me, and all the others. We were all quite numb with shock for a while. Families came to give their loved ones a decent burial. We went to the funerals, one after another. But one young chap had no next of kin, so it was decided to give him a military funeral, and he was to be buried in the small graveyard near the camp. Of course we went to this funeral too, and it seemed all the more sorrowful somehow, this poor young bloke with not even a family member there to see him off. I don't think we would have admitted it, but I think most of us had a tear or two in our eye that day.

Well, of course, life had to go on and our duties with it. A colleague and I had to go on duty the very night of this young bloke's funeral. I don't think we felt like it at all, the whole place seemed to be in the grip of a kind of quiet sadness. It was very difficult to get back into the right frame of mind, but we had our duty to do and we knew we just had to get on with it.

So, we had a few hours' kip, then at 10 pm we went and got our dogs out ready for guard duty. The dogs were acting strange that night; they seemed reluctant to come out of their kennels, which was very unusual. These dogs were German Shepherds, and it was customary for them to leap and bound about when we got them out, they were always full of beans and raring to go. But that night they were very subdued.

We went about our duties as usual, after we had settled the dogs down. We walked the perimeter, and every so often, when we were a little weary, we would stop off in our hut and have a cup of nice hot tea to drive off the sleepiness and cold; then go back to our duties again.

It was a very cold and frosty night, and I remember looking up and seeing the moon round and full. It was that really pale cold colour, but sharp and bright, like it always is on a freezing night in winter. The bloke I was on duty with and me, we'd just had a cuppa, and we were sharing a fag, as I had run out of smokes. We stood outside the hut, stamping our feet in an attempt to keep warm, as we sucked on a Woodbine. The dogs now had become restless, but that wasn't really unusual, as German Shepherds are inclined to be like that by nature. They can be nervy and restless, alert, and aware of everything around them; that's why they make good guard dogs.

As I was standing there, finishing the fag, I was just idly looking out into the moonlit scene before me. Guard duty was often tedious; not much ever happened really. Most of the time we just wished it was all over, so that we could get tucked up into a warm bed and grab some sleep.

Then I noticed something that made me suddenly start. From where we were standing, the small cemetery where the young man had been buried that day was in view. I could see the railings surrounding it and some simple crosses silhouetted in the moonlight. But not only that, I could see something very strange indeed. There was this huge beam of light that seemed to be coming from the heavens. It was far too big for a searchlight. There were no signs, nor sounds of helicopters or any aircraft in the silence of the night. This beam of light seemed to be connecting to where I knew the young man's grave to be. My colleague was watching it too. It was enormous and very bright, and spread out on the ground right where the fresh grave was. It was eerie and we both felt very uneasy, and the dogs had their hackles up and started to whine. We both decided that we would go back inside the hut for a while and have another cup of tea, and if it wasn't gone by then we would have to investigate.

We didn't discuss what we had seen too much when we had our cup of tea, it was like we were both thinking of that dead young man, and we just couldn't figure out what that beam of light meant. I don't think either of us wanted to admit that we were scared by it, but we were.

When we went back out about ten minutes later the beam had gone. It had quite illuminated the grave, making it clearly visible, but now there was just the gentle light of the moon, and we could no longer really distinguish the grave at all. We didn't speak of it between us again, and we told no other members of the camp. I think we were afraid that we would get ribbed. But I shall always remember it, and I do still wonder what that beam of light was and what it meant.'

Everyone around the fire fell silent. Beer glasses had remained full, so intent on the story had been all those listening. No one could come up with any sensible answers. Everyone looked at Bob. He wasn't the kind of man to make things up. He was now a local builder, a rational man, with a wife and three children. Not someone living alone, who might be fond of telling stories for the free drinks and attention.

They remained mystified. No one ever knew what the beam over the grave was all about. And now, probably, no one ever will.

15

The Witch of Burley

In the small and beautiful village of Burley in the New Forest, it is not uncommon to hear tales of witchcraft and peculiar happenings. It is known to be a place where, in the forested areas, bizarre magical rituals take place, even to this day.

Old Dorothy Clutterbuck, the witch said to have initiated Gerald Gardner into the Craft around 1939, was said to have lived in the vicinity. Gerald, of course, is thought of as the founding father of the modern day Wicca religion. Even the 'wickedest man in the world', the Great Beast 666, the occultist Mr Aleister Crowley, is said to have made regular visits to the New Forest. It is a place of magic and mystery, as well as of stunning natural beauty.

Julia wanted to see Burley. So did her best friend Ruth. She and Ruth had started to dabble in the occult. They had played with a ouija board and tarot cards. They had books on spells and how to cast them. They had candles to represent the elements, and perfumed incenses designed with the pagan calendar in mind. They were apt to wear colourful velvet clothing and earrings that depicted flying witches.

So, when Roland and Marcus, friends of theirs from college, decided on a day out, the girls persuaded them to go to Burley. Marcus had not wanted to go; he would rather have gone into Salisbury, found a nice pub, and played pool. But Roland said that was selfish of him, borrowed his mother's Audi, and took them all to where the two girls had been longing to visit.

Marcus protested all the way. He hated the countryside, he proclaimed. It was boring. He insisted that the New Forest was just a load of gorse, trees and ponies. And that the last time he had gone there, a few years back with his parents, he had been stung by a hornet. It really was not a pleasant place to be!

Everyone thought that it was funny his being stung by a hornet, which made him more tetchy than ever. Roland and the girls found that the countryside was pretty stunning. Julia and Ruth were both getting really excited. They just couldn't wait to see this place where there were rumours of naked dancing and drunken revelries, all amongst the trees on a moonlit night. Witches' Sabbats they were called! Even Marcus perked up when he heard about the naked dancing.

It had been raining when they left Salisbury, but now it was easing off. It was only light summer rain anyway, it being early May. The year was 2007. They pulled over to look at their map. They were now only about half a mile from Burley.

'I can feel that this place is full of weird energies,' said Julia. She looked like a colt, leggy and a little ungainly. She had soft brown eyes and long dark hair in a high ponytail. 'Something strange might happen here.'

'Oh, yeah,' sneered Marcus, who had ginger hair and freckles, and looked uncomfortably like Prince Harry. 'Energeees, eh? Well, for a start I'll get drunk, because I'll be sooo bored. Then you might start to see things happen,' he laughed.

'Shut up Marcus!' said Ruth, who was fair, plump and blue-eyed.

'I'm not looking after you if you get drunk,' said Roland, who was popular, as he was a dead ringer for the singer Sting. 'And stop knocking what Julia says. I've seen some pretty spooky happenings around these two girls.'

They drove off again and soon they arrived at their destination. The girls were sitting together in the back and Ruth, craning her neck to look around, exclaimed, 'Oh, wow! This is such a wicked place!'

'Oh, wow, this is such a wicked place,' echoed Marcus, imitating Ruth's little voice and lighting a cigarette. He shook his head. 'It's just another touristy village in the New Forest, that's all. They all look the same to me.' He got out of the car and stretched his long legs. Marcus adored Julia, but wasn't going to tell her. So did Roland. Julia adored neither of them; after all, they would never measure up to the enigmatic members of The Hermetic Order of the Golden Dawn,

Mr Aleister Crowley or Dr Isreal Regardie, not to mention the Wiccan Alex Sanders! Ruth was in love with both Marcus and Roland. Neither of them were in love with Ruth.

'Don't be such a beast, Marcus,' said Julia, getting out and pulling on her long, purple velvet coat.

'Oh Julie, look at those cute little ponies. That one looks pregnant,' squealed Ruth excitedly.

'Like you then,' quipped Marcus. Julia gave him a withering look. Roland looked at the ground and shook his head ruefully.

'Shall we go and touch them, Jul?' asked Ruth, completely ignoring Marcus's remark.

'They probably bite,' said Roland. 'That is what comes from the tourists feeding them. They get bossy over food, and think that everyone who approaches them has some.'

'Horses are nasty like that anyway,' put in Marcus. 'They kick too, the little blighters. You'll not catch me going anywhere near them.'

The girls completely ignored this and went over and petted the ponies, who only nuzzled and nibbled them.

'The shops look interesting,' said Ruth. 'Look at that one! It's called "A Coven of Witches"!'

Both girls laughed at this. Julia's brown eyes widened. 'Ooo, I fancy getting a new tarot pack today. I saw one recently called 'The Witches Tarot', it had some brill pictures. I wonder if they have it in there?'

'I bet they have,' said Ruth. 'And some exciting books, no doubt! I need some candles too.'

The boys crossed the road to join them. 'Let's go to the pub first,' said Marcus. 'Me and Roly need a beer.'

'No,' said Julia petulantly. 'We are going shopping first.'

'I do need the loo though, Jul,' said Ruth. 'Let's have one drink with the boys. I can use the pub loo and then we'll go shopping.'

They found the White Hart, and Marcus, Roland and Ruth went inside. Julia stayed outside and found a bench to sit at.

'You're not getting us to drag around those tourist shops with you two,' said Marcus, bringing out a tray with two halves of lager for the girls.

'Me and Roly are staying in here for a while.'

'Oh typical!' Julia said to Marcus's disappearing back. Never mind. Blokes only get in the way when you are shopping, she thought to herself.

Julia looked around her. There were quite a few people milling about, despite the occasional drizzle. She picked up her lager and took a sip, stretching out her legs and taking in the atmosphere. Burley was a very beautiful place, she decided. It had a vibrant feel to it. She was not disappointed she had come. This was the sort of place where she would like to have a little cottage, a little way into the forest, of course. Yes, a cottage like Terry Pratchett's famous Granny Weatherwax. She could see herself in there, a broomstick ledged by the front door, a cauldron over an old range, a cat or two for company.

In this daydreaming mode she cast her eye around her. There was a family sitting on a bench a few feet away. Mother, father and two children, she presumed. The children were very well behaved. They were quietly munching on a packet of crisps; now and then they sipped at a glass of cola through a straw. Another couple sat way up in the corner of the gardens, billing and cooing at one another like a pair of collared doves. They were middle-aged, and Julia thought them immature. Did people ought to do such unhealthy things in public at that age, she wondered?

Then her eye was caught by the sight of a rather startling looking large lady who was striding down the road with great aplomb and, what was more, on her left shoulder there rode a glossy, cheeky-looking jackdaw!

Julia couldn't stop staring at her. The large lady looked directly at Julia and gave a knowing smile. Julia, slightly embarrassed for staring the way she had been, lowered her eyes and nervously put a strand or two of loose hair behind her ear. When she looked up again, the large lady was very close to where she was sitting. The jackdaw was cawing and bobbing on her shoulder. Then it opened its beak and made a strange noise, very similar to a frog croaking.

The large lady was looking directly at Julia again now. Her eyes were rather fine, and twinkled with a kind of mischief that somehow complemented her pet. Julia caught a sense of fun from both of them that made her want to laugh out loud. At that moment Ruth came back. 'There was a queue for the loo,' she explained, 'but it's a lovely old pub inside. Marcus has downed two pints already. Roland is being good though, as he's driving. He's only got a half of bitter, which he's hardly touched. He's wonderful!'

Julia had turned to her friend as she had arrived. When she looked back to where the large lady and the bird had been standing, she found that they were gone. She got up quickly, ran out and looked up and down the road. There was no sign of them anywhere. How could they possibly have disappeared so quickly? It was not as if they were inconspicuous!

'Did you see that lady with a bird on her shoulder when you came out just now?' Julia asked Ruth.

'You what?' Ruth looked puzzled.

'Obviously not, then,' said Julia, mystified.

'A lady with a bird on her shoulder?' Ruth frowned. 'It's not something you see every day is that.'

'A jackdaw actually,' said Julia. 'How you didn't see her I'll never know. Are you sure you didn't see her? She was larger than life. And the bird …'

'She must have gone just before I got out here,' said Ruth. 'Bet we'll see her again when we go walking around the village. I hope so anyway! How bizarre!'

Julia shuddered a little. She had a creepy feeling about it all now. She didn't know why. It was a feeling that she could not really explain. She drank up her lager and let Ruth chatter on. But she remained quiet.

Soon the boys came out to join them. Roland had twisted Marcus's arm to go round the shops with the girls. After all, he had said, it really was their special day out. They should be humoured.

The first place Julia headed for was A Coven of Witches. She wanted to do something down to earth like spending some money. When they got inside, they found the shop to be full of all sorts of treasures: crystals, candles, incenses, figurines of witches, wizards and dragons, crystal balls, witches' skrying balls, and books on spells, magic and astrology. It was a never-ending Aladdin's Cave of the weird and wonderful.

Julia was so busy looking at all those things that it took a while before she noticed a picture on the wall.

Then she suddenly exclaimed, 'Oh my God! There she is!' she clapped a hand to her mouth.

'There who is?' asked Ruth, rather startled.

'The lady with the jackdaw!' said Julia. And indeed, there in the picture was a large lady, with a jackdaw on her shoulder.

'That is dear old Sybil,' said a voice from behind them. The girls turned to see a man. He was serving in the shop. 'Sybil Leek. She used to run an antique shop here. She is, in fact, Burley's famous witch!'

'Really?' asked Ruth, but she was staring at Julia.

'Yes. Have you not heard of her before then?' asked the man.

'No,' said the girls in unison.

'Well, she never went anywhere without the jackdaw. She said it was her familiar.' The man laughed and went on, 'She told everyone that the Great Beast himself, Aleister Crowley, had initiated her into paganism. She was quite a prolific writer on occult matters in fact. But she was not popular with the locals at the time, nor members of the church for that matter. They say she was hounded out. But I don't know. She eventually went to America, where she kept writing, and I think appeared on television. She certainly was quite a character.'

Julia's head was swimming. The lady in the picture was definitely the one she had seen walking down the high street just now. She had never heard of her or seen her before today. She felt quite faint.

Ruth was staring at her, wide-eyed.

'But Julia,' she said, 'you saw that lady walking around here today! You told me before we got here.'

'Impossible,' said the man. 'Sybil Leek has been dead this many a year. She died out there in America, an old woman.'

16

The Ghostly Pianist

In 1982 at the turn of summer, the time when it loses its vitality and decides to slip into autumn, two elderly ladies travelled together to Lymington to take a holiday break. They had managed to book themselves into the very same hotel that they had shared with their husbands a few times in the good old days, when the men were still alive. They had often holidayed together, the four of them, all being firm friends, and always up for a laugh, a meal and some conversation.

When the two ladies arrived at their destination, they were pleased to see little change in the town. It was thriving, as ever, with its charming gift shops and the little art galleries that they loved to frequent. Not to mention the shops selling all the scrumptious local food produce.

They were in Lymington for a long weekend and they both fully intended to enjoy the break. The weather had remained fine, and still rather warm for the time of year. Ada and Iris had dressed themselves in similar cool linen jackets, with loose-fitting trousers. Ada wore lavender, Iris cream.

After they had checked in at the hotel and had a much needed pot of tea, the ladies took a taxi down to the harbour and watched the boats bobbing and the screaming gulls soaring. The sea breeze whipped their silk scarves awry, and untidied their hairdos, making them slightly breathless. They giggled like schoolgirls. They felt almost young again. The sparkle came back to their eyes, the roses to their cheeks. They walked in a sprightlier manner. They linked arms and nibbled at choc-ices, and felt refreshed.

And so the halcyon day went on for the two friends. They explored the town all over again, as if it were a stranger to them. They laughed raucously as they mounted high stools in a wine bar, and a handsome young man in a tuxedo served them with cool Pinot Grigio. They had never been in a wine bar before and couldn't decide what to ask for! The young man had gallantly chosen for them. And they both agreed, as they sipped the fresh white wine, that it tasted very good.

They spent the next afternoon at the harbour, walking and enjoying the air. They finished off by sitting on a bench, with a slice of haddock and some golden chips eaten from the packet, which had been wrapped in newspaper. The sun played on the water and, in the distance, they could hear music coming from on board one of the boats. They sat and dreamed.

That morning they had found an old bookshop near the centre of town, dusty and quaint. It was run by an elderly, rather elegant gentleman. Ada quite fancied him but Iris declared, in a whisper into her friend's ear, that she thought that he was decidedly gay. Ada had indignantly, and rather loudly, replied that there was nothing wrong with that. In fact, she loved a jolly man. She couldn't bear a miserable one. Iris convulsed with laughter, to the astonishment of her friend. They shared the joke later, when they had left the shop.

The man in the bookshop had said a strange thing, though. He had announced, right out of the blue, that Ada was a psychic. Both ladies were astounded at this. Neither knew anything about psychics. Ada declared that the only psychic she had heard of was Mystic Meg, and her Joe had said that she was a journalist, and not a psychic at all. Iris said that she had heard of Betty Shine and Doris Stokes. Ada said that they were not psychics, were they? Didn't they talk to the dead? They agreed that they had heard of Uri Geller – but both decided that Ada could probably not bend spoons! So they ended up giggling about it and then promptly forgot it all.

It was on the last night of their stay in the hotel that something peculiar happened, something that afterwards they both found very hard to explain. They had just finished a rather good dinner in the dining room – sorrel soup, followed by chicken breast in a garlic sauce with parsley, and fresh vegetables. For pudding they had had a splendid strawberry shortcake with lashings of thick, golden, local cream. Iris had decided to be extravagant on their last evening and had ordered a half bottle of champagne to go with the shortbread. She had heard that the combination was delicious! They were not disappointed. They ended with Italian coffee, a shot of brandy, and some dark chocolate squares.

Replenished, they rather tipsily agreed, as they sat now in the lounge, where they had taken themselves with their coffee, relaxing in deep green leather chairs, that they had both had a fine time and would be booking again next year.

As they sat there, facing a pretty, but unused, inglenook, under muted green lamps, they reminisced about former years. They talked about when they had been courted by Joe and Giles. Joe, Ada's husband, had then been in the army; Giles, Iris's husband, in the navy. How handsome they had been in their uniforms! They remembered the visits to the cinema, the walks in the New Forest, the visits to the seaside and the tea dances. Oh yes, the tea dances! Ada laughed and wiped away a tear at the same time. How Joe loved the tea dances and to hear the piano played, as it always was on those occasions! Eventually they wobbled their way up to bed, arms linked, to steady themselves. They went to their room. They had opted for just one; it was economical to do so. And, besides, it was very comforting to have a friend share a room in a strange place at night. And they could chat to one another before sleep, as they had used to do as girls, when they would stay at one set of their parents' house or the other. They had been friends for many years. It was not long before both fell asleep in their twin beds, though. The champagne and brandy had relaxed them wonderfully well.

Something startled Ada from out of her sleep. She instinctively reached out, switched on the Art Deco bedside lamp, and stared at her watch. It said 2.30 am. She peered over to the next bed to see Iris still sound asleep, mouth slightly open, softly snoring. Ada sat, head cocked, listening. Yes, she could hear a piano playing – that is what had woken her.

She listened again and heard a Cole Porter song being played. Yes, she was sure it was a Cole Porter. It was coming from downstairs; she thought it might be from the direction of the lounge. Funny that. She had not noticed a piano in there. Someone was playing it in a rather expert manner. It sounded very professional. But it was quite late to be partying on a Sunday night in the hotel lounge, surely?

Ada went over and gently shook Iris awake. She asked her if she could hear the wonderful music. Iris, bleary-eyed, grumpily said that she could not, and would Ada please go back to bed! She shut her eyes and turned over.

Ada, sighing at her friend's obvious reluctance to explore and slipped on her rosebud covered towelling dressing gown. She went downstairs, intending to peep at the partygoers. Maybe they would invite her to join them, to listen to the music? What fun that would be! What an exciting end to the holiday! Iris would be upset in the morning if she knew she had missed this.

But when Ada got downstairs, she was astonished to find the bar all closed down, the lights dimmed, and absolutely no one around! The lounge was quite empty. And, what is more, there was no piano in sight! All was totally silent everywhere.

Soon, a tired looking member of staff appeared, obviously having heard Ada's exclamations. She asked if madam was all right, in a courteous but rather disgruntled manner. Ada enquired if there was a piano in the hotel. The young lady raised her eyebrows slightly and replied that no, there was no piano in the hotel, in the way that hotel staff do when they have to reply to unusual and outrageous requests from eccentric guests. Ada then asked if anyone had been playing a record player or the radio rather loudly just now? The young lady cleared her throat, scratched her nose, and said absolutely not. It would be against hotel rules to have loud music playing at this time of night! Bewildered, Ada decided to go back to her room. The young lady watched her go, shaking her head.

Ada related all that had happened to her friend, as they were leaving the hotel the next day. Iris thought this over for some time, before turning to her friend and saying, 'Perhaps the man in the bookshop was right, Ada – maybe you *are* psychic?'

17

The Black Dog

Ian Dursley was travelling home in his Ford Escort. The year was 1971. It was a cold and rather clear February night. There was a gibbous moon, winter pale. The stars were scintillating, crowding the night sky. There was a cold breeze that sent the clouds scudding over the moon, blocking her out, then reappearing, peek-a-boo.

Ian was in a good mood. He could hardly wait to get home and tell Judy, his wife, that things had gone very well with Bill Sterney, and that Bill had decided to take him on as apprentice thatcher. A very good job to have! Ian whistled a tune as he drove. He had stayed a bit over late at Bill's house in Chirton, over the Wiltshire border. But what did that matter? He was on his way home to Andover now. Bill loved to chat. And it was all worth it anyway. He had employment again!

He was no more than a mile from Andover, perhaps less, when his car died on him. He freewheeled into the side of the road, pulled over and stopped. He tried restarting the engine. It wouldn't turn. He got out and fiddled with a few things under the bonnet, took off the spark plugs and wiped them, then put them back on, got back in the car, and tried to start it again. No luck. He got out again and kicked the door of the car. Darn old banger! Never mind, things would pick up enough soon for him to buy a new car.

He turned up his jacket collar against the cold wind of the night. He was so close to home now he might as well walk. What was a mile or two on a clear night? Besides, he was so full of good spirits. He could almost see the smile on Judy's face when he told her the news. It had been a bit of a tough time for both of them lately. And he knew how much Judy wanted to start a family. Now that he had employment again and the chance to earn good money, perhaps they could think about it.

He had so much in his head, the good news and what it meant, that at first he was not aware of the feeling that crept up on him. At first he thought it was just the cold. The clear night produced a breeze that chilled. He shivered a little and tucked his hands deep in his jacket pockets. He sunk his head down into his collar, looking under the lids of his eyes at the road ahead.

All was quiet. It was past midnight and most folks had gone to bed; there was no other traffic on the road. Ian glanced at the pallid moon. A few strings of black cloud, like the nets of fishermen, veiled her now and then. He didn't know why, but suddenly he had the uncanny feeling that something, or someone, was following him. He instinctively looked behind him. The road fell away in the moonlight, thorn hedges on either side. There was nothing there. But still the eerie feeling remained. He still felt as if something was behind him, following him, at a distance, just out of sight.

'You are gettin' fanciful, me laddie,' said a voice, and he was startled, almost, to find that it was his own. He quickened his pace, head bent, heading in the direction of home. He had thought for one moment to go back to the car. But what was the use? He would get Brian, his brother-in-law, to come to help him with it in the morning. Brian was a wizard with engines, he'd get the old banger going! If not, he'd tow it back with his truck.

The feeling came back as he marched on, though. And it was not just a feeling now. He could hear something behind him. It was a panting sound, like that of a dog, and a click, click, like its claws on the road, always a few feet behind. His mouth was beginning to go dry. He wanted to turn around but some self-preservation instinct told him not to. He wanted to run. But he felt that it would be useless. It could catch him easily. Whatever *it* was.

He stopped dead, plucked up the courage and turned around. There was nothing there. Absolutely nothing. The road was stonily silent. Tussocks of grass on the verges, still wilting and lame from the winter, were silhouetted in the moonlight. The thorn bushes were black against the sky. That is all that he could see.

He walked on nervously. Soon the road sign declared that he had arrived in Andover. He breathed a sigh of relief. Not far now until home. He forced his mind on thoughts of the cottage where he lived with Judy – the warm sitting room with the comfy sofa; the lights on to dispel darkness; the logs aflame in the hearth. Fire and light. Keep thinking fire and light.

But the darkness crept back in as he heard the panting again, and the soft footfalls, with the click, click, click. It was behind him again, whatever it was. And it was preternatural. Of that he was now quite sure. It sounded like a dog. But it did not feel like a dog. He had had many a dog in his life. Dogs he did not mind. But this … this was different. Think fire and light. Think fire and light.

He felt something touch the back of his leg. He swung round automatically. He stood rooted to the spot at what he saw. It was a huge black hairy form. It stood at least four feet high at the shoulder. Its mouth hung open in a pant; a gaping maw. Its head was huge, as big as a bear's, and its ears erect. But it was the eyes that were the most terrifying. They were two saucers of swirling red light. Ian felt a malevolence come from the animal, such as he had never experienced before. His mouth opened in a horrified scream. He felt the sweat of fear break out all over his body. He thought that the creature was going to attack him. And so afraid was he that he just stood, petrified, like a rabbit in the headlamps of a car. He thought that he might pass out. It was at this point that the creature just turned and quietly walked away. It did not look back, but disappeared into the distance, its black shape finally merging into the shadows. Ian stood looking after it, shaking with fear. Sweat beaded his brow and his hands had gone clammy. Then he ran and ran, on trembling legs, all the way home.

Judy had waited up for him. She had been worried by his lateness. When she saw the state he was in, she felt full of foreboding. She quickly put the kettle on and made a hot drink. Soon she had him sitting down on the sofa. She bent and removed his boots for him. He was white with shock and still trembling. Eventually he told her his story.

Judy did not question its validity. She just sat dumbfounded, her face a picture of anxiety and concern. She had heard of such stories before;

her parents were both country folk. It set her mind racing in a flurry of worry.

'Oh Ian!' she said, 'you've seen the Black Dog. Do you know what that means?'

'I don't know what it was, love. But I saw it all right! What do you think it means?'

'It means ill fortune. That's what it means.'

'Ill fortune? But surely not? I was coming home so full of good news; with all of this, I forgot to tell you. Bill Sterney has taken me on as his apprentice. I got the job!'

Judy was silent. The longed for smile did not break on her face. She said nothing; she did not want to speak. She wanted badly to share in her husband's joy, but it was marred. He had got the good news. But he had then seen the Black Dog.

Two days later news came that Bill Sterney had been in an accident. He had fallen from his ladder and broken his back. He was in a bad way. They thought that if he lived, he would never walk again. There was now no job for Ian.

Six weeks later Judy's mother died. Her father could not cope alone. She went back to live with him for a while, glad to be out of Ian's company for a bit. He had got despondent over the loss of the job and depression had set in. He found solace in the bottle. Instead of searching for work he lay around and drank. In the evenings he would frequent the pubs and keep bad company. Judy did not return to her husband. Although she loved him it was all too much. He was frequently seen thereafter, sitting in the corner of some local pub, hunched over a drink, unkempt in appearance and sick in soul.

Some of the old folks would shake their heads and say when they saw him, 'He got the Black Dog on 'is shoulder, that one.'

18

The Smugglers

In the summer of 1959 Martha and George Covington had been on an outing to Portsmouth from their home in Rowlands Castle. They had enjoyed a boat trip and had picnicked on the harbour. It had been a successful day, organised especially for the pensioners of the area and thereabouts.

The only fly in the ointment had been that the coach driver was nowhere to be seen when they were supposed to have left Portsmouth. This resulted in them all being home later than they had really wanted to be. George, Martha and the rest of the pensioners had taken it in good heart, though, despite the minor annoyance of all concerned. One by one they were dropped off until George and Martha were the only ones left. They lived in Finchdean Road.

The coach driver dropped them on the Petersfield road, near to Leigh Park. They would need to walk through the village and under the arches to Finchdean Road. It was past midnight, but George and Martha didn't really mind the walk. It was a warm night and they had had a good supper of fish and chips, with a few glasses of ale to wash it down.

So off they set for home, arm in arm. They talked about their day. They were happy that the weather had held so well. Meeting up with friends had been good. Martha particularly loved the boat trip. George said the fish and chips were second to none. Martha had some pebbles in her handbag, a keepsake of the outing.

There was no moon so it was quite dark. In fact they had difficulty in seeing where they were going. As they got to the big beech trees of Stansted Park it seemed even darker; no lights were on anywhere because of the time of night. They held on to one another, stumbling in the pitch blackness.

They had not gone much further when, about 20 yards ahead of them, they saw a light. It was quite odd, as it seemed to be an old fashioned lantern, lit by a candle. It flickered and moved as if someone was carrying it. Yet there seemed no possibility of that, as it had appeared so suddenly, and there was no impression that anyone had come from a side path or that anyone had struck a match to light it.

As George and Martha walked on, the light was up ahead, as if guiding them. It was swinging, giving the impression of being carried by a handle from the top, yet they could hear no footsteps and there was no illumination on the feet or legs of the bearer of the lamp. It was uncanny; it really was as though the lantern was lighting the way home for them. And, despite the strangeness, they felt grateful for it. The path was so dark that they would have had much greater difficulty in negotiating their way otherwise.

They followed the light for some time, but kept on asking one another how the lamp could be moving up ahead without a carrier. George insisted that someone must be carrying it. But Martha pointed out that no one could be seen. They were mystified, but did not really feel afraid. It was very odd. Lanterns like that were rarely seen now, let alone lanterns that did not seem to have a bearer!

Very soon they found themselves at their own front gate. As they turned to go in, they noticed that the lamp up ahead had disappeared completely from sight.

'Well, I'll be darned!' exclaimed George, as he set foot in his front garden.

'Well there!' said Martha. 'It's gone and disappeared! What do you reckon to that?'

In the days that followed Martha and George marvelled over their strange lantern guide. Neither could come up with an adequate explanation. They were both very curious as to the answer but none came.

Then, one day, months later, Martha wanted George to go to his allotments and gather some produce for the WI stall. Martha was famous for her baking and sold it on the weekly stall, along with some of the delicious fresh vegetables her husband had grown on their allotment.

It was a lazy day at the end of September, almost summery apart from the fact that you could feel that the sun was dying. George made his way down to the allotments with a new hoe in his hands. When he arrived he saw an old fellow who was not usually there. They called a greeting to each other. No one else was around. Late bees buzzed and a blackbird hopped over the ground, looking hopeful that some earth might be turned and a worm or two found.

It transpired that the newcomer, who turned out to be ninety-two, was a father of one of the allotment holders, and he himself had been a local until he had moved after the war. George went into his shed, put the kettle on the spirit primus, and made them both a mug of tea. They sat on the bench at the bottom of George's piece of allotment, under a crab apple tree covered in the bitter little ripe apples, and sipped at the hot honey-coloured brew.

Eventually, as they chatted, George related the strange story of the lantern that had guided him and Martha home that night in the summer. The old man went quiet for a bit, drank his tea, and tapped his hobnail-booted foot as if in time.

'Oh, you be seeing the smugglers,' he said, in a quite matter of fact way.

'Smugglers?' George was intrigued.

'Oh, ah,' said the old man. 'Langstone to Rake; an' on northwards. Went all along what is now Finchdean Road, the smugglers' route. That be the smugglers' lantern you an' the wife be seein'. You ain't the fust, nor will be the last to see it.'

'Well there! You believe in ghosts then?' asked George incredulously.

'Well, I'd be right daft not to, seein' that I seed it meself wi' me own eyes, long afore thee.'

19

The Dream

Sylvester and Jasper were sitting on the veranda taking morning tea. It was something that they both delighted in when the warm summer mornings came, and the red geraniums that Sylvester carefully tended were in bloom.

They had moved to the New Forest when Jasper had retired from the Civil Service. Sylvester had been a sound technician, then a director, in several small theatres around the country. He would still sometimes go off to some theatre or other to do some work for them, but mainly now he enjoyed a leisurely life with Jasper, his partner.

Jasper's dream had been to have an old country house in the New Forest area; and this now had been achieved. Sylvester had been unsure at first, preferring the apartments they had shared in Bath, in the centre of the city. But, he soon came to love the countryside, its quietude, and the relaxed existence they now led. And, after all, if he felt too stifled by it, he could flee back to the city on the pretence of work.

The house they shared was 16th-century, all peaks, leaded windows and raftered rooms. It perpetually smelled of beeswax and turpentine, as Jasper had lavishly furnished it with antique pieces that he lovingly polished himself, not trusting the cleaning lady with them. It had five bedrooms and was set in about an acre and a half of beautiful gardens. Jasper adored it. But Sylvester always felt as if he was being watched by some invisible presence. Jasper thought Sylvester rather highly strung, and told him straight that theatrical influence was at the root of his feelings.

That summer morning in June 1974, very near to the longest day, Sylvester, sitting on a white cast-iron chair with its plump green velvet cushion, sipping at his Earl Grey tea, announced that he had had a very strange dream the night before.

Jasper, nibbling at a piece of toast with thickly-cut marmalade, hardly looked up from *The Times* as his partner spoke. Jasper had no time for dreams and whatnot. He decided not to humour Sylvester. It might send him off on a torrent of words that would end up being a long, long story. So, instead, he just ignored his companion and commented on some news of the day, as if he had not heard.

Being snubbed, Sylvester left the table and went to deadhead some of the sweet scented roses that lined the drive. After about half an hour he found Jasper at his elbow, his straw hat on, dressed in a rather fine white linen suit. He announced that he wished to go to Beaulieu and take a look around. Sylvester looked astonished for a moment, and then, knowing how impatient Jasper could be if he were kept waiting, ran off to change from his dressing gown into a pair of jeans and a tee shirt.

Soon they were in their Mercedes and travelling along the forest road towards Beaulieu. It was a passion of Jasper's to explore any area in which he lived, especially for things of archaeological or historical interest. Today, it was Beaulieu. Very soon Jasper was rattling off all his knowledge about the place – the house, the motor museum, the abbey. He knew all about it theoretically, now he was going there to experience it first-hand.

Sylvester was strangely silent. Usually he would listen with awe to Jasper's superior knowledge of these things, and sometimes timidly ask a question of two. If Jasper noticed the silence, he said nothing. He kept up his running commentary of the history of Beaulieu all the way until they arrived.

They spent a pleasant morning enjoying first the motor museum, then the splendid house and grounds. After they had stopped for a coffee and a cup cake, they went to the abbey. When they had passed through the lay brothers' day entrance, Sylvester came over quite faint, and asked to go and sit on a bench in the cloisters.

Jasper was soon sat next to him, quite concerned. This was most unlike Sylvester. He hoped that he was not ill. Sylvester sat awhile, not speaking. He seemed as if in a dream. Then he suddenly looked up and said, 'What do you know about Sir Arthur Conan Doyle?'

Jasper was perplexed. 'Um. He was of course the author of the famous Sherlock Holmes stories. He was a medical doctor. I think he liked to dabble in the paranormal. Wasn't he one of the ones who believed in those fake pictures of fairies those little girls hoaxed? Why on earth did you suddenly mention him, of all people?'

'It was because of that dream I had last night,' Sylvester replied.

'Oh come now, Sylvester, come.' Jasper got out a snowy handkerchief and wiped his brow. Sylvester had given him quite a turn, getting faint like that. 'I've told you before that you have a habit of letting your imagination run away with you.'

'But you haven't heard what I was going to say!' remonstrated Sylvester, vehemently.

Jasper could see there was nothing for it but to humour him. Perhaps he would be able to persuade him to go to the GP and get his blood pressure checked on their return. 'Go on then, tell me,' he said.

'Well, I have never been here before but I know every inch of this abbey, Jasper. I saw it in my dream!'

He then proceeded to point here and there and to say what was inside every door and every walkway. Jasper looked at the guidebook, which they had not opened as yet, and, sure enough, Sylvester was quite correct.

'Are you certain that you've never been here before?' asked Jasper. 'Not even as a child?'

'Never,' said Sylvester, emphatically. 'I swear.'

'But what has this to do with Sir Arthur Conan Doyle?'

'Well, the dream began with a group of sitters at a séance,' continued Sylvester. 'This man sitting amongst the others at the table I recognised as Sir Arthur Conan Doyle. I have seen his picture many times. We have, of course, done theatre productions of *Sherlock Holmes*. There were other gentlemen at the table, and some ladies. An elderly grey-haired woman was conducting the actual séance. Then the dream changed; you know how it can swap from one place to another in dreams, in a flash, don't you?'

'Yes …,' said Jasper, now quite intrigued, despite himself.

Sylvester swallowed hard before continuing. 'Then suddenly we were here. In this very abbey at Beaulieu! It was as if I were with them.

It was the group of people at the séance again, Conan Doyle amongst them. They were walking around, admiring everything. And then, as plain as day, I heard Sir Arthur say that it was a very inspiring place and that he would surely write a novel around it some day. We continued to saunter around. Some of the things have changed, of course, but most were the same as in the dream. And, Jasper, you can imagine how astonished I was when you suggested we come here today!'

'Indeed, this is quite extraordinary!' said Jasper. 'You really did know your way around, despite never having been here before … but one thing doesn't ring true. I don't know of a novel that Conan Doyle wrote with anything to do with Beaulieu in it, do you?'

Sylvester looked a little crestfallen at this. 'No, I don't either.'

When they arrived back home, Jasper went straight to the library. He did not come out again until dinner was on the table. He joined Sylvester in the dining room, sat down, and poured himself some good claret, and put a book on the table right next to him.

'Listen to this,' he said, taking a forkful of roast beef and swallowing it before picking up the book. He opened it at a marked page. 'Conan Doyle wrote a novel called *The White Company*. It is a knights-in-armour tale of chivalry and adventure; a story of heroic knights, and a boy who must chose between the life of the monastery, or the adventures of travel and war, and of love too. Alleyne Edricson, the boy, had been in the shelter of the abbey at Beaulieu in Hampshire, when his choices arose.'

Sylvester's eyes were like saucers. He put down his knife and fork. 'Then Conan Doyle did write a novel that involved Beaulieu Abbey?'

'It seems like he did. Well there! I never knew that,' said Jasper, shaking his head.

'Nor did I,' said Sylvester, 'but it was in the dream, wasn't it?'

Index